Love You

LORNA JANE CLARKSON

Love You

LORNA JANE CLARKSON

Contents

This is
about you.

It's about feeling fit, strong & ALIVE.

It's about turning your back on negativity & starting afresh with oozing CONFIDENCE.

It's about radiance, positivity & an abundance of good old-fashioned ENERGY.

It's about adopting an "anything is possible" attitude & becoming who you were always meant to be— beautiful, vibrant & totally UNSTOPPABLE.

It's about learning to LOVE YOURSELF.

It's all about YOU.

THIS BOOK IS ABOUT YOU.
It's about giving you the
encouragement to invest in
yourself, back yourself,
push yourself, improve yourself
and ultimately love yourself
inside and out.

THIS BOOK IS FOR YOU.

It was written for you, to
inspire you, to motivate you and
to let you know that who YOU are
and what YOU do with your life
actually matters.

This is for you

Across the globe, women have vastly different challenges, opportunities, hopes and dreams. But I think we all have the same basic desires – to find purpose, fulfilment and the satisfaction that our lives are as good as they possibly can be.

We fill our days with endless busy-ness but often fail to stop and think about where we're going in our lives. We say we have big dreams and want to achieve success, when in reality we get so caught up in our everyday routines and obligations that our lives become stagnant and a little disappointing. Our days become less about what we want to do and more about what we feel we 'have' to do.

I think you deserve better. And I've written this book to inspire you to create a better life for yourself. To show you how to put yourself first, and encourage you to start living your life with passion, confidence, positivity and more love than you could ever have imagined.

I'm Lorna Jane; Activewear designer, food fanatic, lover of life, big dreamer and believer that anything is possible. I'm completely obsessed with all things health and fitness. I'm a make-it-happen kind of girl and I openly confess to being an eternal optimist.

I've worked hard to create a life that I love and it all started twenty years ago, when I sat down to ask myself where I wanted to go with my life and what it was that I really wanted to do.

These were pretty tough questions and I'll be honest with you, I didn't have all the answers straight away. But it did start me thinking about how I was spending my days and, ultimately, how I was spending my LIFE.

At the time, Lorna Jane (the brand) was still a start-up business, 7 years young and going gang-busters. I'd gone from being a dental therapist looking at teeth all day to being a designer of my own label which was a dream come true. I was creating a new category in fitness apparel and it was an exciting time, but there was something missing.

I started designing Activewear because I wanted to inspire women to workout, but there was always a voice in my head asking me if I could do more. Could I do MORE to inspire women to embrace a positive and healthy lifestyle – and possibly strive for more in their lives too?

I didn't know it at the time, but the answer was YES.

> **MY LIFE DIDN'T HAPPEN BY ACCIDENT. I PURPOSE BUILT IT FOR MYSELF.**

Over the years my life and my brand have grown into something that has the ability to actually change women's lives – and that is what inspires me! Empowering women and building a global community of like-minded ambassadors was certainly not part of my initial plan, but it has grown to be my true passion and what I hope will be my life's legacy.

I want to inspire YOU to live your life at 100%.

And what I've learnt is that you have to work on yourself first. You have to take the time to discover who you are, learn to love and accept yourself, and then go about building an incredible life.

In this book I give you insights into my own personal journey with self-love, but also show you how to let go of fear, chase down your dreams and find the courage and the willingness to make the important things in your life happen!

Nobody's life is perfect. And I'll also share with you some of the many challenges that I've faced in my life and my business as well as so many of the things that I believe have given me both happiness and success. I'll talk about my daily rituals, show you my go-to workouts and share some of my favourites recipes in the hope that they will become your favourites too.

Over the years I've spoken a lot about my Active Living philosophy and the daily practice of Move, Nourish and Believe and I'll talk about it more in these pages because, it works! It's easy to incorporate into your daily life, and is the one thing that has kept me energised, focused and abundantly healthy. In fact it's the philosophy on which I have built my entire life.

This book is for YOU.

This book was written for YOU, to encourage you and to guide you into creating an amazing life for yourself.

When you pick up this book I want you to stop and read the title every single time. Say it out loud or simply say it to yourself, but say 'LOVE YOU' to the most important person in your life.

Because believe me, when you invest the time to focus on yourself, are willing to believe in yourself, work on yourself and truly learn to love and appreciate yourself... You will find that anything really is possible!

Fall in love with YOURSELF first.

CHAPTER ONE
Fall in love with yourself

I believe that everyone deserves to live a life that they love, and that life can only begin when you start to love yourself and truly accept yourself for who you are.

To bring out the best in yourself, you must first learn to love yourself.

So let's talk about self-love...

They say the most important relationship you have in your life is the one that you have with yourself, and I couldn't agree more. Self-love is one of the most powerful emotions you will ever experience and, contrary to popular belief, has nothing to do with being selfish, conceited or thinking you are better than anyone else.

Self-love is about having self-respect, a positive self-image and unconditional self-acceptance. It's about having a healthy regard for yourself and knowing that you are a worthy human being. It's about understanding that you have just one body to look after, one heart to nurture and one life to chase down your dreams.

> DON'T FORGET TO FALL IN LOVE WITH YOURSELF FIRST.

But, in a world where women are often raised to put others first, setting aside time for self-love can cause feelings of guilt and we can often struggle to maintain a dedicated self-love practice. It's frustrating because we know that we need self-love but we have difficulty giving ourselves permission to experience it.

We need to FIND the time to practise self-love so that we can re-connect with ourselves and live a life that truly shines; a life where we keep growing, learning and feeling good about ourselves a little more every day.

Here are my favourite ways to practise a little self-love:

1. Learn to put yourself first... even if this means not being totally available.
Decide that sometimes, staying in, giving yourself a facial, making bliss balls and drinking tea, is going to nourish your life more than going to that party with friends.

2. Be yourself... without seeking the approval of others.
That's right - dye your hair pink if you want to, decide to take a year off work and go trekking, go and see a movie by yourself, dance in the living room and enrol in that class you've always wanted to do. Don't seek permission to be yourself, simply give yourself permission to do so.

3. Accept yourself for who you are... the good the bad and the ugly.
Decide what you like about yourself. Celebrate it! Learn to accentuate your favourite characteristics and play-down the not-so-shiny ones (we all have them!)

4. Own your beauty inside and out... Even when you are makeup-free, your hair's a mess, or you're super sweaty after your workout.
Own it and love yourself for who you are.

5. Nurture your body...
Give your body the nurturing, rest, exercise and fuel it needs to perform at its best. Active bodies need rest to recover just as much as they need more exercise to stay energetic. Find your balance and do what's right for YOU.

6. Make time to do what you enjoy without worrying about wasting time.
If you enjoy a day on the couch – have a day on the couch. It's not a waste of time if you find enjoyment in it and it's not like you do it every day.

7. Speak your truth... don't swallow words that express how you truly feel.
Choose to find a nice way to say what you think, even if it's harder than telling a lie. Speaking your truth may seem more difficult at the time, but it's always the right thing to do.

8. Learn to set boundaries... especially for protecting and nurturing your relationships.

Spend time with the people that you love and remember that the relationship you have with yourself is the most important. 'Me time' is not something you should ever feel guilty about.

And most importantly:

9. Love and accept yourself even when you fail miserably.

Let me guess, you didn't get the job? You came last? You didn't pass? You forgot something really important? We've all had those trials and tribulations. What's important is that after it's all over, you still love yourself.

Like most worthwhile things in life, self-love takes practise so don't expect to master everything straight away (nobody does!). Be kind to yourself and understand that learning to love yourself is a lifetime investment.

Know that only you can bring out the best in you, so simply promise yourself that you'll keep working on it every day.

LOVE YOURSELF – BECAUSE YOU'RE BRAVER
THAN YOU THINK, SMARTER THAN YOU KNOW,
TWICE AS BEAUTIFUL AS YOU'VE EVER
IMAGINED AND GETTING STRONGER EVERY DAY.

CHAPTER TWO
The world needs what you've got

 SHE WOKE UP EVERY MORNING WITH THE OPTION OF BEING ANYONE SHE WISHED, HOW BEAUTIFUL IT WAS THAT SHE ALWAYS CHOSE TO BE HERSELF.

— *Tyler Kent White*

Over the years I've learnt to be unapologetically myself and I'm here to tell you that who you are and what you decide to do with your life matters. So it's important that we talk about authenticity, and that you take the time to stop and ask yourself 'am I really being myself?'

Being yourself seems pretty self-explanatory: just wake up, eat what you want to eat, say what you want to say, do what you want to do, and live how you want to live... But trust me, it can be a lot harder than we actually realise.

Sometimes you think you are being yourself when the reality is that you're being a 'version' of yourself to please other people.

UNTOLD STORY: I THOUGHT THAT THEY WOULDN'T TAKE ME SERIOUSLY IF I WORE MY ACTIVEWEAR

I remember way back in the early days of my career, when I was asked to talk to a group of women or students about myself and my business. Everyone wanted to know about Lorna Jane 'the entrepreneur', so for some crazy reason I thought I had to present myself as a 'business woman'. I would madly write out a formal speech, stand at the podium and address the audience like a politician with pages of notes. And to make matters worse I would pry myself out of my Activewear and force myself into a business suit and high heels because that's what I thought they wanted to see.

What was I thinking?

Looking back now, it seems insane that I could get it so wrong, ME the girl that only ever wears Activewear, talking about my Activewear brand in a business suit and high heels.

I thought I was being myself - but that wasn't the case.

And then I realized - being myself meant wearing my Activewear because that's what I do every day. Being myself meant speaking from the heart (without pages of notes) because that's how I believe we should speak to each other. And ultimately, being myself meant connecting with people on a deeper level by having a two-way conversation instead of just standing on a stage and talking about myself.

So the next time I had a speaking engagement, I pushed all of the negative talk about living up to expectation and possibly disappointing everyone, aside and went out there and gave them who I was and it felt amazing! My message was clearer, it felt easier and more natural, and my connection with the audience was so much stronger and more personal. Everyone loved it and so many more women came to talk to me afterwards because I think I was just so much more relatable and obviously more approachable.

I learnt just how important it is to believe in who you are and to know that being yourself is always good enough. That it's important not to feel pressured to do things the same way as everyone else, because doing things your way is better for you. I learnt that when you allow yourself to 'be yourself' then everything really does just effortlessly fall into place. And now I KNOW that the world needs what I've got and being authentic is important.

So, let's talk about authenticity.

Being authentic means coming from an honest place within. It's when our actions and words align with our core values and beliefs. It is about being our truest self and not a watered down or spruced-up version that we think other people want to see.

What was getting in the way of my authenticity was my lack of confidence and the pressure that I put on myself to please other people. I was taking the path I thought I SHOULD walk instead of listening to my intuition and doing things the way that I knew would feel more natural for me.

If you want to be authentic it takes finding the courage to be yourself. And in a time where authenticity is increasingly more difficult to find and to define, it couldn't be more important.

Authenticity starts with the intention to be genuine and here are some of the things I think are important to get you started.

1. Get to know who you are and be that person...
When you act authentically it becomes so much easier and feels more natural to express yourself with honesty and integrity.

2. Follow your own common sense and value system...
Learn to tune-in to your intuition. When something feels right - follow that feeling. Understand when something feels wrong and choose not to walk that path.

3. Seek advice from others but always trust your gut...
Always listen to another's point of view but remember to always weigh things up and do your own research. Trust yourself to make the right decision for you because you're the one that has to live with the result.

4. Recognise, appreciate and develop your own unique talents...
Hone your skills, become a master of something, not an all-rounder of nothing.

5. Appreciate that being different is a gift...
Embrace everything that makes you unlike anyone else. Whether it's physical, emotional or mental, use these differences to your advantage.

6. Stand up for what you believe in...
Get up, speak up and shake things up! The world needs bold leaders. The world needs what you've got.

7. Love yourself for who you are...
You are in charge of who you are so love every part of you - what's not to love?

Remember, your life isn't yours if you're constantly caring what other people think of you. The world needs what you've got so why not run your own race, work on your authenticity and rediscover who you really are.

BE YOURSELF AND YOU CAN BE ANYTHING.

CHAPTER THREE
You're not designed for everyone to love you

 DON'T CHANGE SO THAT PEOPLE WILL LOVE YOU, BE YOURSELF AND THE RIGHT PEOPLE WILL LOVE YOU ANYWAY.

We live in a world of more than 7 billion people, so when you think about it, there's bound to be someone out there that you just don't like - and vice versa. I would honestly love to be able to say that everyone in the world is one big happy family but the reality is that we are not, and chances are we never will be.

Everyone's entitled to their own feelings and opinions. We all come from different races, religions, countries and cultures - so we're bound to have vastly different views. Of course we all need to learn to respect one another and treat each other with kindness but we must also try not to take any negative feelings to heart or let them stop us from being our most authentic selves.

As highly social beings, we so often become worried and bothered by what the world thinks of us. We burden ourselves with worrying about how we are perceived, so we try to fit in, to please and to gratify others. How often have you caught yourself laughing at someone that you don't really find funny or nodding your head in understanding when you actually disagree? Unfortunately, this happens to the best of us and many would argue that sometimes, it's simply a matter of being polite.

I think, to an extent, this is true and on occasion we choose to sacrifice our own ideas and ideals in order to be courteous and respectful. But, when it comes to the essence of YOU and your own personal message to the world – what you choose to say, how you choose to act and how you choose to think - worrying about being liked will only cause restraint and limit you in your life.

*YOU'LL NEVER CHANGE THE WORLD IF
YOU'RE WORRIED ABOUT BEING LIKED.*

- Robin Sharma

I know for a fact that some people think I'm a little too perky, overly optimistic and that I talk about health and fitness way too much. But do I play down these characteristics to gain approval and be liked by everyone? Absolutely not! This is me genuinely being myself and I've learnt that some people will love me (which is great) and other people will think that I'm just a little too much.

And that's ok, because I know I'm not designed for everyone to like me.

I think it's important to be at peace with our 'quirks' and learn to love who we are – our age, our shape, our lack of musical talent, the freckles on our skin – whatever they are!

Because once we let go of trying to please everyone and realise there is so much more to life than being popular or being liked, we discover that we never really needed to 'fit in' and that we definitely don't need other people to validate or accept us.

You just can't waste time worrying about what people think. Your focus and responsibility must be first and foremost to yourself, to remain true to yourself and to know that you don't have to prove anything to anyone.

You are amazing so remember that!

Remember that you are truly special for who you already are and at the end of the day, what you make of your life is totally up to you. So, stick with the people that make you feel like you don't have to change. Dare to be original in everything; your thoughts, your actions, the way you dress. Change your mind if you want to but most importantly don't worry about what other people think about you. You're not designed for everyone to like you, so go ahead and do what YOU want to do with your life.

BE YOU AND RELENTLESSLY YOU.

-Lady Gaga

CHAPTER FOUR

We're not meant to be perfect

Guess what? I'm not perfect.

I speak out of turn, I care too much about certain things and I try to get everything done in an impossible amount of time. But I don't see these as things I need to change about myself. Instead, I choose to look at them as unique qualities that make me who I am!

So what is perfection?

Perfection is an illusion and just in case you haven't worked it out yet - no one is perfect – not the girls you follow on Instagram, not your favourite celebrities, not your seemingly flawless best friend or even Ryan Gosling for that matter (yes, I said it - even Ryan!)

Perfection is a story that we create in our mind that doesn't really exist, and if you're serious about loving yourself, the chase for perfection needs to be one of the first things you recognise and eliminate from your life.

I think, the most frustrating thing for me is that we all KNOW perfection doesn't exist, but we still continually exhaust ourselves in the pursuit of it. Are we chasing it because we think people will like us better, we'll be more popular or possibly become happier when we reach it? Or do we honestly believe that perfection will fulfil us?

Let's think about this for a moment; who are all the people in our lives that we love and admire? And why do we love them? Is it because of their brilliant careers, their beautiful homes, perfect children or impressive six-packs?
I don't think so!

In fact, it has nothing to do with any of these things and is more about the way they make us feel when we're with them, their endearing flaws and human failings, the fact that they find our jokes funny or simply because we can be ourselves around them.

It's perfectly wonderful to be IMPERFECT!

So, why then do WE strive for perfection in ourselves when it's not what we actually look for in other people? And why would we possibly think that they're looking for or expecting perfection from us? The wonderful truth is they aren't.

I'm always saying to my husband when I've been particularly annoying or stubborn over something –that it's those less-than-perfect things about me that he'll miss when I'm gone! You know what I'm talking about – cold feet in bed, stealing the last piece of chocolate, inviting people to stay and not telling him until the day before or simply falling asleep in front of the television and refusing to go to bed no matter how many times he tries to wake me!

It's who we are when we allow ourselves to forget about trying to be perfect that makes us more loveable. And I believe these quirks and characteristics are exactly what makes us interesting and much more fun to be around.

People are not perfect, but they can be perfect for each other and I personally think it's pretty amazing that we all have our own unique qualities, favourite things to do and people to spend time with. I have to admit that I like standing out from the crowd, having a different point of view and being less than perfect.

I think chasing perfection holds us back from actually loving ourselves and accepting ourselves for who we really are. And while we're talking about perfection (and not chasing it anymore) I'd like to talk a little bit about beauty and what it really means to be beautiful.

To me, beauty is the exact opposite of perfection and has so little to do with how we look.

I believe that true beauty lies in the way that we think and the most amazing kind of beauty is the kind that comes from within. The beauty that starts with learning to love yourself first and then letting that love flow on to everyone else in your life.

You know the kind of beauty I'm talking about – the one that lies in strength, kindness and compassion. The type of beauty that's associated with caring words, good work and being an all-round decent human being.

Now, I'm not saying that we shouldn't care about how we look, but what I am trying to emphasise is that we can all get a little off-track sometimes, giving our external beauty more credit than it really deserves.

We need to fall in love with WHO we are. Accept the things we can't change about ourselves and work on the things we want to improve - but never, ever, ever strive for perfection.

Remember that kindness is beautiful. Compassion is beautiful. Honesty is beautiful. Vulnerability is beautiful. And loving yourself is beautiful.

So stop chasing perfection and just be yourself.

I'VE DECIDED TO BE BEAUTIFUL, NOT BY HAVING THE PERFECT BODY OR WEARING TONS OF MAKE-UP – BUT BY LOVING MYSELF FOR WHO I AM.

- Lorna Jane Clarkson

UNTOLD STORY: A FRIENDLY REMINDER
ABOUT WHY WE ARE LOVED

I was in Sydney in the lead up to Active Nation Day. I was also doing some TV appearances and endless media back-to-back and I remember being a little stressed about what I was going to wear and what my hair looked like and who was doing my make-up.

I made a comment to my girlfriend, who I was staying with at the time, about how I wished I was in better shape, how tired I was looking, how dry my skin was, and my hair, and she looked me straight in the eye and said 'what makes you think for a single minute that people are coming to see you, or even 'like' you because of what you look like?' She then went on to tell me just how amazing I was, how important my message was, and let me share with you that there was not a single word in her dialogue about outward beauty.

Of course, we have been friends for a very long time and she is completely biased AND she was delivering the speech of a lifetime to build up my confidence; BUT I learnt a lot that day.

It was a timely reminder for me about what's important in life; that what you say has more value than how you look, that your appearance is not why you are loved, and that we should put more effort into WHO we are and what we stand for than what we look like!

All things that I already knew, but obviously needed to be reminded of and who better to deliver it than one of my dearest, dearest friends who is always there for me with the honesty and openness that I treasure more than she will ever know (unless she reads this – which she probably will!)

How we look on the outside is such a small part of who we are and why people like us. And to recognise this (or be reminded of it) is life-changing because it frees you up to put less energy into how you look and concentrate more on who you are and being yourself.

HEY BEAUTIFUL, IT'S TIME TO
START BEING HAPPY WITH YOURSELF.

Stop wishing you looked like
someone else. Stop trying to get
attention from those that don't
appreciate you. Stop hating your
body, your face, your
personality, your quirks. Love
them. Because without those
things you wouldn't be you.
Smile like you mean it. Embrace
who you are. Learn to love and
accept your flaws and cherish
your imperfections because they
make you, YOU.

And you are AMAZING.

CHAPTER FIVE
Stop comparing

Tell me, when you look in the mirror, what do you see? Do you see what others see? That beautiful girl with a generous spirit and passion for life? Do you see how enchanting your eyes are? How wonderful your hair looks with the sun shining on it? And your compassion, sense of humour and contagious smile?

Do you see and appreciate all of these beautiful things in the mirror? Or are you constantly comparing yourself to others?

In this modern world of social media, where everything is enhanced with filters and made to look absolutely perfect, we can easily get caught up comparing ourselves to other people and their seemingly perfect lives. We become dissatisfied because we're unrealistically measuring everything we have (and don't have) with the lives of people that we don't even know.

We've all been guilty of this from time to time, but it needs to STOP. Stop comparing yourself and your life to other people – because if you spend all of your time watching and wanting to be someone else then when will you ever find the time to work on being yourself and living your own magnificent life?

We don't measure our intelligence against Albert Einstein, so stop trying to stack up physically against Gisele Bündchen.

Let me tell you that wanting to be someone else is a waste of the person you are. So forget about what everyone else is doing, where they are going and who they are hanging out with – and put all your efforts into BEING YOU.

I know from personal experience that I achieve more, and feel so much more confident when I stop worrying about what everybody else is doing. Remember, you were put on this planet to experience YOUR LIFE, not someone else's. So forget about playing the comparison game and instead choose to love yourself, be yourself and live your life as only you can.

    ALWAYS BE A FIRST-RATE VERSION
 OF YOURSELF INSTEAD OF A SECOND-RATE
    VERSION OF SOMEBODY ELSE.
          - Judy Garland

your time is
LIMITED
so don't

waste it living someone else's life.

- Steve Jobs

CHAPTER SIX

Love and support each other

 WHEN WOMEN LOVE AND SUPPORT EACH OTHER, INCREDIBLE THINGS HAPPEN.

I know that right now is an amazing time in history for women. We have so much to celebrate, but we still have a long way to go, especially when it comes to supporting each other. As women, we all know how hard it can be to smash glass ceilings and fight gender stereotypes. But what I don't understand is why we continue to make it harder for each other when we know how difficult it can be for ourselves?

Why are women so competitive with other women when we have so much to gain by supporting each other?

Please know that celebrating another woman's success does not take away from your own, rather it collectively means we are more successful. Supporting another woman does not take away from your strength; it means that we all become stronger. And sharing your wisdom with other women does not make you foolish; it makes you a fountain of knowledge and inspiration. We do not lose anything when we give to other people. In fact, we GAIN.

Like many women in business and particularly women in the spotlight, I have been on the receiving end of scathing comments, bitchy remarks and unfounded accusations on more than one occasion. And I'm not afraid to say that it hurts every single time!

I don't often talk about it because I don't like to give negativity more oxygen than it deserves, but with the intention of putting a stop to this trend of attacking women I'd like to share with you how I felt when it happened to me in such a public way.

UNTOLD STORY: TRIAL BY MEDIA

It should have been the experience of a lifetime: '60 Minutes' was doing a profile piece on me and my company and suddenly, in the middle of filming, my world was turned upside down.

We spent the day shooting up at Noosa and were driving home when I got a frantic call from my PR Manager that 'A Current Affair' was running a story about a girl that was accusing us of 'bullying' and 'fat-shaming' her whilst she worked at Lorna Jane. And to make it even worse she was attempting to sue us for half a million dollars - I was in shock.

Here was someone publicaly accusing us of doing something completely against our working culture – and to make matters worse, the media was taking her side and telling the world!

This was just the beginning of possibly one of the most challenging times in the history of Lorna Jane - and every single person working for us (not just me) felt under attack.

We banded together and kept our chins up but, unfortunately, it didn't stop there.

More articles started popping up across a multitude of media outlets with past employees also claiming that they had experienced the same thing. We couldn't believe it. Of course as a big business, it's hard to know every single thing that happens across some 150 stores with over 2000 employees, but we approached every individual about their accusations and they all vanished without a word. To me, it felt like there was a sinister plot against us that we couldn't make right, no matter how hard we tried.

There was endless name-calling and nasty remarks on our social media platforms, and people even went so far as to say hateful things to some of the girls that worked in our stores.

Let me be totally transparent here, if it had not been for the undying support of my darling husband, my family, my wonderful friends and amazing team at Lorna Jane I would have walked away during this time. Because no matter how strong you think you are, when you are being unfairly attacked on such a large scale it becomes completely unbearable. My heart was broken and there were days when I simply did not want to get out of bed – I just wanted to hide from the world and wake up when it was all over.

I find it astonishing that the media can print things based on hearsay and that other people feel the need to then say terrible things about you when there are so many other positive things they could be doing with their time. Why do we have this magnetic attraction to negative talk about people – especially people in the spotlight? We need to remember, they are still human and contrary to popular belief, they don't deserve to be treated this way. Here's a thought – why not write positive stories, celebrate people's success and make the world a more uplifting place?

When I look back now, I think what hurt me the most was the fact that I had been working for so long to inspire and empower women with my brand and then with one unfounded accusation it felt like it was all for nothing. The public (and the media) were so quick to disregard all of the incredibly empowering things that we had done for women and instead chose to get caught up in the negativity of one story.

Whatever happened to the phrase 'innocent until proven guilty' or is it 'trial by media' that we're talking about here? And I'm not just talking about the professional media who have the power to initiate these things but also social media that has the power to creep into your personal space and make it impossible to escape the barrage of criticism.

I'm sharing this story because I truly believe that we should love and support each other, and because I hope that it will make you think twice before you judge someone based on what you hear about them or what you see in a magazine or on TV. Know that not everything you hear or read is true! And that false media has a direct impact on people's lives, it can affect profitability of companies, cause loss of jobs, destroy relationships and in extreme cases lead to anxiety, depression and possibly suicide – all for a catchy headline.

I've learned, that what people say about other people or what is printed on the pages of a blog or a magazine says more about the people who are sending that message than the message itself. It isn't a coincidence that any negativity in our lives comes from a handful of the same people, TV shows and magazines.

Please, be a woman that supports other women (or anyone for that matter.) And start today with some simple ways to show you care:

Show them that you believe in them... We all experience self-doubt from time to time. So why not be there for the people in your life to show them that you believe in them and encourage them to keep moving forward in the good times and the bad.

Share your knowledge... Don't be afraid of teaching other women how to do something that you're good at. You won't be any less good at doing it yourself. If you know how to bake a great cake, it won't taste any worse by giving someone else the recipe.

Give compliments... They are totally free and always make people feel good. The next time you admire something about another woman - tell her! Even if it's a stranger on the street or someone you follow on Instagram – compliments are always worth more when they're unexpected and they can make a bigger positive impact on someone's day than you think.

Be nice... Just stop talking about other women in a negative way (especially when it comes to appearance and what they're doing with their lives.) If you've got nothing good to say about someone then don't say anything at all.

Get behind each other... There are so many reasons why women's voices are not always heard and one of the most common is lack of confidence. We can help change this by getting behind other women and supporting them and their ideas. Put yourself in someone else's shoes. Wouldn't it be nice to have someone backing you all the time?

> AS WOMEN, WE MUST STAND UP FOR OURSELVES.
>
> AS WOMEN, WE MUST STAND UP FOR EACH OTHER.
>
> AS WOMEN, WE MUST STAND UP FOR JUSTICE FOR ALL.
>
> – Michelle Obama

CHAPTER SEVEN

Start with believe

 BELIEVE YOU CAN AND YOU'RE HALFWAY THERE.
– Theodore Roosevelt

Show me an extremely successful person, and I'll show you someone who believed in themselves. Steve Jobs, Oprah Winfrey and Beyoncé are all examples of highly successful individuals who benefited greatly from their own confidence and self-belief.

They are living proof that when you start with BELIEVE you open up the possibility to achieve great things in your life.

As I write this, I'm sitting in my LA home. We have recently opened our 250th store – and I just had to pinch myself. My family have come to visit from Australia, which is making me reflect a little and I'm feeling an overwhelming sense of gratitude for all the amazing opportunities that have got me to this point in my life and I honestly owe it all to BELIEVING in myself.

Did I think I would be sitting here, writing my 5th book? Not in a million years! But did I commit to believing in myself the whole way here? You bet I did!

When I started my business, I was the one and only entrepreneur in my family. I didn't have anyone to learn or gain experience from but for some crazy reason I trusted that I would figure everything out along the way. I believed in myself and I know that this confidence has been the difference for me time and time again.

Even though I knew I didn't have the knowledge or all of the talents to get me to where I was going, I believed that I had the ability to learn these things and improve myself along the way. I knew my strengths and I knew my weaknesses. But more importantly I was willing to test, experiment and try new things even when I was uncertain. I was prepared to fail because I believed in myself enough to know that if I fell, I would be able to pick myself up again.

Believing in yourself is not about never falling, but more about getting back up again when you do.

I knew I was good at designing Activewear and I knew I could inspire women. But what I also realised was that I couldn't achieve everything I wanted to achieve on my own. I knew I wasn't good at the commercial side of things. I knew I didn't feel comfortable in a business environment and I knew for sure that I couldn't crunch numbers. But what's important is that I didn't let any of these insecurities stop me.

As crazy as my ideas may have seemed at the time, I didn't listen to the people telling me that it wasn't going to work. Instead, I chose to believe in myself and to surround myself with people who shared my vision. I made the decision to trust that if I just kept moving forward, I would figure things out along the way.

This is what I think sets successful people apart from everyone else. They don't wait for intelligence, resources or opportunities before they start chasing their dreams. They don't care how many times they have to fail to make it happen. They look for opportunities instead of obstacles. They seek out people who say 'YES', they forge paths where there is nowhere to walk and they build bridges where there is nothing to walk on.

In every situation they KNOW they will eventually get to where they want to be, no matter how many face-dives they have to experience along the way, because they choose to believe in themselves.

I am convinced that everything good in life starts with believe – and no matter what it is that you want to achieve in your life, trust me, self-belief will get you 100% closer to making it happen.

Self-belief is the tool that allows you to discover, harness and master your unique talents and limitless potential. In fact, it is the key ingredient to bringing your 'hidden' talents to life. It takes you from singing in the shower to singing on a stage; from sitting quietly in a meeting to standing up and voicing your opinions; and from being afraid of heights to sky-diving on the weekends.

Start by taking your dreams seriously. So you want to write songs, win MasterChef or start your own business? If these are your dreams, don't joke about them - believe in them! Share them with people openly and honestly, talk about what you hope to achieve. Believe in yourself enough to know that with hard work, dedication and focus, you will make it.

Start here. Start now. Start believing in YOU!

UNTOLD STORY: BELIEVE IN YOURSELF EVEN WHEN THEY TELL YOU YOU'RE CRAZY!

Do you know how many times I've been told that I'm crazy?

I started designing Activewear because I wanted to inspire women to workout. I clearly believed that if I could design feminine pieces that were also functional, then she would look forward to her workouts and actually workout more.

But let me share with you that when I started on this journey EVERYONE thought I was crazy - and they weren't afraid to tell me either.

They thought I was crazy to think that women would wear Activewear outside of their workouts. They thought I was crazy to think I could open a store that just sold Activewear. And they thought I was crazy to think that Activewear could actually inspire people to be fitter and healthier!

Fast forward 28 years and now people ask me - 'Did you ever think that women would be wearing their Activewear everywhere and that your brand would be an inspiration to women all over the world?' And I say - 'Are you crazy? I've been talking about this for as long as I can remember!' But they couldn't see it until it happened.

You have to believe in yourself (especially when no one else does), because when you have a unique vision (like Activewear everywhere), when you are trying to create change or when you simply have a dream that is bigger than most - you will be called 'crazy'.

THERE IS NO FORCE EQUAL TO THAT OF
A DETERMINED WOMAN.

Your
PURPOSE
in life is to
find your
purpose.

CHAPTER EIGHT
Dream bigger

Big dreams are the reason why the world changes for the better. They're why we have new discoveries, great inventions and find cures for diseases. I love big dreams because they have the power to move our minds, lift our levels of self-esteem, boost our self-confidence and make us feel more positive about ourselves.

But, what I love the most about big dreams is that they give us the opportunity to truly leave our mark on the world.

MY BIG DREAM: TO DESIGN ACTIVEWEAR THAT WOULD INSPIRE WOMEN

When I started Lorna Jane, my dream was to create an Activewear brand that inspired women - a BIG dream back in the nineties, but one that I could see as clear as day. Only a handful of people (and that's being really generous) thought it was possible at the time. But I knew I had to take the chance, give it everything I had and at least try to make my dream come true.

It would have been so easy to listen to all of the naysayers who were telling me that going up against the likes of Nike and Adidas was 'crazy.' But in my dream it wasn't like that! My dream was about creating a new category, creating something that didn't already exist, it was about changing the way women thought about their Activewear.

My BIG dream allowed me to have a clear vision of what I wanted to achieve and that vision was so powerful that I was able to make it a reality. Even today, I can close my eyes and visualize that same dream. And I believe without a doubt that the more we picture our dreams, the more we are able to make them happen.

My dream worked because I did the work - I had the vision, I had the determination and I had the fortitude to endure the challenging times to see it through to the end.

> **DREAMS ONLY WORK IF YOU DO THE WORK.**
> — *LORNA JANE CLARKSON*

I believe there are enormous benefits to having big dreams. But I also know that you need to be willing to put in the hard work every single day to make them a reality. We all have our dreams for the future, but unfortunately so many of us give up on them. All too often, we throw in the proverbial towel and go back to what we were doing before – back to the comfort of what we know, back to what we find easy.

With that in mind here are some tips on how to dream big and get closer to making your dreams a reality:

1. Get inspired...

One of my favourite ways to discover like-minded dreamers and doers who overcame their critics, is to read up on other people's stories. Strong women like Oprah or JK Rowling. Fearless females who were all told NO before they were told YES. Women who were so determined to make their dream come true, that they never stopped pursuing what they wanted.

2. Write down your dreams...

The busy nature of life can often mean that our dreams get pushed to the side. Write your dreams down on a piece of paper and carry it with you or stick it somewhere prominent to serve as a daily reminder. Why not start by putting 10 minutes aside each day to write down your dreams. I find the first few minutes in the morning are perfect for this (or just after yoga) - my mind is less cluttered and there's a clarity about how I want to feel and what I want to achieve.

3. Visualise your dreams...

I've found that dreams work so much better when you can visualise the outcome. You don't have to close your eyes (but you can.) Just imagine what your future will look like when you achieve your goals and start living out your dreams. Envisage every detail. Put yourself in the future and try to feel it. The power of positive manifestation is second to none when it comes to chasing your dreams.

4. Take action...

We must do everything we can to achieve what we want. So break your dreams down and do something small towards achieving them every day. Trust me, taking small steps consistently will get you to where you want to be in less time than you imagined.

5. Track your progress...

Hold yourself accountable by putting regular checks in place along the way. You won't always stay on track (and that's ok) but if you don't monitor your progress, you won't feel as though you're going anywhere.

6. Find support...

It's really important to share your dreams with some like-minded and positive individuals that will encourage you and more importantly hold you accountable. I do this all the time and I cannot tell you the number of dreams that would not have happened if my husband, my Mum or my friends hadn't prompted me along the way!

7. Accept failure...

Disclaimer: If you have big dreams you need to be prepared for some bumps along the way. Every big dreamer has failed more than once in their lives (myself included.) So be prepared to fail many times to succeed just once.

8. Push negativity aside...

Don't let anyone hold you back. There will unfortunately be people that tell you your dreams are too big but it's your choice whether you listen to them or not.

Remember, dreams only work if YOU do the work. And trust me there will be so many people that will question you and place doubts in your mind. Whether it's your dream job, a new and exciting business or simply getting fitter and healthier, never let it be said that your dreams are a waste of time.

> YOUR LIFE HAS PURPOSE.
> YOUR DREAMS MATTER. AND YOU WERE
> BORN TO MAKE AN IMPACT.

UNTOLD STORY: NEVER LET OTHER PEOPLE'S OPINIONS STOP YOU FROM CHASING YOUR DREAMS

I've had my fair share of people trying to talk me out of my dreams and one in particular comes to mind because the ending proves that even people with the best of intentions can get it wrong sometimes.

I had already quit my day job and was making Activewear and teaching classes full-time. I had a studio in one of the biggest fitness centres in Brisbane but I wanted to expand into retail and open up my first concept store.

Bill and I had done the research - we knew how many pieces we had to sell to cover our rent (I think it was about 10 per week at the time.) We were going to work in the store ourselves so we wouldn't have to pay wages and we thought we could make a pretty good go of it.

We had done the groundwork and now all I had to do was let the owner of the fitness centre I was currently working and selling from, know about my plans and to let him know I was leaving.

Allan was a friend of mine and someone who I looked up to as a business owner and as a person. We sat down and I enthusiastically told him about my big dream and plans for the future expecting him to be excited for me - which unfortunately wasn't the case.

He thought I should keep my business small, and that going into retail was far too risky and he asked why would I want to put more pressure on myself when I was making such good money where I was and paying so little rent.

Here was someone I deeply admired, and I guess the most successful business person that I knew at the time - telling me my dream was too big!

I was shattered. Totally shattered and it took everything I had not to breakdown in tears. Luckily I managed to keep it all together until he left the room, but then the flood-gates opened and I literally cried for hours. I look back now and realize that his words were just the tipping point for all of my fears and insecurities to come to the surface. It forced me to ask myself some difficult questions and face the fact that I was going to come up against scrutiny and other people just like Allan no matter what.

The good news is that I came out of my studio a little red-eyed and swollen but even more determined to make my dreams a reality.

And the best part of this story is that as soon as I opened my store I never heard another negative word about it from Allan. In fact 15 years later when I had stores all over Australia and was being recognized for inspiring women through my work, I received a phone call out of the blue from him to congratulate me on my success.

We hadn't really had a conversion for at least 12 years but he had seen an article about Lorna Jane in the paper and called to apologize for trying to talk me out of following my dreams all those years ago and to tell me he was so very proud of me and glad that I didn't listen to his advice.

Looking back now, I think his initial reaction to my BIG dream actually could have made me even more determined to make it work. Either way I cherish the fact that he reached out to me and want him to know that his kind words of support and belief in me now - mean so much to me and always will.

TRUE BELIEVER

WORLD CHAMPION SURFER & MOTIVATIONAL SPEAKER

Layne Beachley

WHAT IS YOUR BIGGEST
ACCOMPLISHMENT?

Winning my 7th World Title and creating a successful speaking career after retiring from professional sport.

NAME SOMETHING YOU ARE PROUD OF.
JUST ONE THING?

I'm proud of the legacy I have created in the world of surfing and the difference I make in other women's lives through my Aim For The Stars Foundation.

WHAT DOES LOVING YOURSELF MEAN TO
YOU?

True acceptance. If you can look at your reflection in the mirror and say the words 'I Love You' without looking away from your gaze, you are there. It takes practise, discipline and commitment to love yourself. It also means you take (non-negotiable) time out to nurture yourself on a daily basis.

WHAT DO YOU DO IN ORDER TO PRACTISE
SELF-LOVE?

I do something I love every day - surf, meditate, yoga, learn, immerse myself in nature, laugh, share my struggles with others and listen to my body.

WAS THERE EVER A MOMENT IN TIME
WHEN YOU STOPPED BELIEVING IN
YOURSELF? HOW DID YOU OVERCOME
THIS?

There have been many times when I stopped believing in myself, both as an athlete and as a business woman. If I find myself making excuses, lobbying others, rationalising (AKA speaking rational-lies) or seeking validation I am out of flow and in a state of self-sabotage. You can't change what you can't see so when I

find myself in any of these states I first acknowledge that I am feeling uncertain or fearful and ask myself 'why?'. In these moments I also rely on my network of honesty barometers, friends and colleagues who bring the best out in me and provide me with clarity and perspective.

WHAT DO YOU THINK IS YOUR BEST
QUALITY AND WHY?

Humility. I don't take myself, or others too seriously and refuse to be placed on a pedestal. What you see is what you get. Keep it real.

WHO IS YOUR BIGGEST ROLE MODEL
AND WHY?

I actually don't have a role model as I don't want to be like anyone else but me. I draw inspiration from others such as my dad, my husband and other successful people. I have become a role model to others by staying true to myself.

WHAT DO YOU HOPE OTHER WOMEN
WILL LEARN FROM YOUR STORY?

None of us are born champions or success stories. I wasn't born a world champion! Living a life you love and self love is about knowing what you want, choosing those you want to be surrounded by and living according to your highest values and never compromising on them.

IN 25 WORDS OR LESS WHAT IS YOUR
MESSAGE TO THE WORLD?

Live. Love. Laugh. Never Give Up.

YOUR FAVOURITE INSPIRATIONAL
QUOTE:

'It's choice, not chance that determines our destiny.'

CHAPTER NINE
Do what you love

 FIND WHAT YOU LOVE, DO WHAT YOU LOVE, BE WHAT YOU LOVE.
— Lorna Jane Clarkson

Are you one of those people who dreads the thought of waking up in the morning and heading to work? Maybe you haven't felt motivated lately or even the slightest bit interested in what you're doing? Maybe you stare at the clock all day, counting the hours until you're free?

Well, you're not alone. In fact, you're in the company of hundreds of thousands of people who aren't doing what they love. But the good news is it's never too late. No matter how old you are or where you are in your life, you can still follow through with your dreams and do what you love.

I often hear the words 'find your passion" being thrown around and I think this is where most of us get stuck. Let's stop thinking about the word 'passion' in our search for a more fulfilling life and start to think about the things that we simply love to do.

I'm talking about doing the things that get your heart racing, the things you always look forward to and the things that make you feel the most excited in the whole wide world. These are the things that you need to create more time for in your life.

Even if you're just doing what you love as a hobby or a side gig to start with, do them often because you never know when the opportunity will come for them to grow into something more.

So often when you just put yourself in 'the right place' opportunities can present themselves and I have seen this happen so many times at Lorna Jane.

Over the years I have seen so many enthusiastic, young women who love the Lorna Jane brand take any job available just to get their foot in the door.

I'm impressed by their vision. And I love the fact that they believed in themselves enough to know that it didn't matter so much where they started, they just knew that their talent, hard work and passion for the brand would be seen and eventually make their dreams a reality. They took the opportunity to put themselves in a place where their talents would be recognized, they worked hard and they have grown into amazing individuals that are now a huge part of our daily success.

If you know what you would love to do, then be prepared to start at the bottom. If you want to write for your favourite magazine, just take ANY job there. If you love horses just see if you can do some work at a local stable on the weekends. And if you want to work in film then volunteer your services on the weekends. Put yourself out there and get involved – it might just be the stepping stone to a life that you love.

And I guess the same goes for starting your own business, you can't expect to create your dream life in day one – you have to be prepared to start with nothing and work for everything!

I love what I do, but I didn't just wake up and start leading a design team and running a global business! I started from the ground up... I was a 'Lorna Jane of all trades' – designing, cutting, sewing and even selling on the weekends. I had to do so many things that I wouldn't put anywhere near my 'love to do' list. But I knew that all those long days and sleepless nights wouldn't last forever and that they would make me a better designer, a better marketer and a better leader today.

When you do what you love it's not going to be sunshine and butterflies all of the time. But it doesn't seem to matter because you're living your dream and, like anything in life, you have to be prepared to take the good with the bad!

The only way to do what you truly love is to wake up every day and DO IT.

But, what happens if you don't know what you love? The truth is that there isn't a one-size-fits-all formula for figuring it out, so forget about having that 'eureka' moment of clarity and understand that for most of us, finding what we love can be through a series of small, seemingly insignificant discoveries.

And here are some things to try when figuring it out:

1. Ask yourself some honest questions...

I think sometimes we're too scared to be honest with ourselves because we don't want to challenge the status-quo of our current lives. Be brave and ask yourself: what would I spend my time doing if I didn't have to worry about money? What interests me? What kind of movies, books or documentaries could I watch to find inspiration? What do I love to do more than anything else?

2. Try to remember things that you loved to do as a child...

Maybe you were a wannabe actress, astronaut or acrobat? Whatever it was that made you smile as a kid probably still makes you smile now. That same girl is still somewhere inside you. Use your fondest memories to discover any forgotten things that you love to do. These experiences and childhood dreams often tap into our most innate sense of self and show us what we truly loved before life got serious and we became conditioned to the world around us.

3. Listen to your friends...

Make a note of all of the things that people tell you you're good at. It could be organising meetings, making delicious food, choosing the right clothes or simply making people laugh and feel good about themselves. It sounds obvious but so often these things can help you channel your calling in life. Could it be that you are good at these things because you love doing them? And should you pursue them a little further? I think YES!

4. Make some lists...

This activity is a 'no-brainer' for me – I love writing lists (if you haven't guessed that already.) Because I find that writing things down in list-form always gives me clarity.

Things I love to do vs. things I don't like to do.
Things I do every day vs. things I want to do every day.
Things I want to try.
Things that make me happy.

Have a look at all of these lists and see what aligns. Where are the commonalities and what is standing out to you? If you find that your 'things I do every day' and 'things that make me happy' lists don't have any matches, maybe it's time to re-evaluate?

Life is too precious to sit back and wait for something to happen. Find what you love, do what you love, and keep doing it – because chances are it will lead you somewhere beyond amazing.

> BY DOING WHAT YOU LOVE, YOU INSPIRE
> AND AWAKEN THE HEARTS OF OTHERS.

CHAPTER TEN
Be fearless

 BE FEARLESS IN THE PURSUIT OF WHAT SETS YOUR SOUL ON FIRE.
-Jennifer Lee

I'm constantly telling myself to be fearless but when I stop and really think about it, no matter how many times I practise my 'Wonder Woman' pose – I still have serious doubts that being fearless is even possible.

Maybe what is possible is using fear to channel my energy in a more positive way to overcome it. Maybe what I actually need is a little bit of conquered fear in order to be fearless. And, maybe, learning how to harness my fear is the most fearless I can expect to become.

Too often we allow fear, worry and self-doubt to dominate and define our lives. We let it steal our opportunities, our confidence, our happiness and our precious dreams. We allow our fears to take hold of us, stop us in our tracks and paralyse us.

But what would you do if you didn't have fear? Would you climb a mountain, travel the world, enrol in salsa classes or launch your own website? No matter how big or small, it's important to recognise that the fear that's stopping you is just a feeling – a story that you have created in your head about what could possibly happen – but that made-up story is not real!

If you look at any great brand, inspiring business or successful career you'll find that there has always been an element of fearlessness or risk-taking involved in their success. A time or many times when someone has had to step outside of their comfort zone, go into unchartered territory and try something a little scary for the first time.

The capacity that these risk-takers have to do this, when everyone else is playing it safe, is exactly what separates them and makes them great.

It takes courage to face your fears and do something for the first time, but so often it is the tipping point to being a leader in your field and becoming exceptional at what you do.

Finding courage and taking risks isn't easy (for anyone) but it's exactly what needs to happen in order to move forward and do great things with your life.

So how can we become more confident? Push doubt to the side and become a little more fearless?

1. Recognise that fear is just a feeling...
Unless what we fear is literally life threatening, then fear is just a story that we have created in our minds about what might happen. And even though we need to listen to our fears, we should also be reminded that most of our fears are wasted worries that never actually take place!

2. Ask yourself what you are really worried about...
When faced with something I fear, I have learnt to ask myself 'What am I truly worried about, deep down?' If I can, I work out what's holding me back and what the worst possible outcome could be. It allows me to put everything in perspective and make the best possible decision.

3. Plan for failure if it should happen...
Write down the worst possible outcome of facing your fear and then come up with an action plan to overcome it, just in case. Think of the worst case scenario but don't let it rule your decision to be fearless.

4. Change your thinking...

Create an irresistible, compelling and pleasurable reason to face your fears. If you don't then you'll come up with an excuse not to face them every single time.

5. Adopt a daring mindset...

Don't give time, attention or energy to fear – take a deep breath and go for it. More often than not you'll be surprised to find that it wasn't that bad after all.

Facing your fears is about letting courage and confidence sit in the driver's seat. Like everything else, the more you do it, the easier it becomes and the faster you'll be able to drive. Yes, it will be scary every single time and you won't always be sure that you're doing the right thing, but one thing I know from personal experience is that - nobody ever overcame fear without facing it.

IN ORDER TO SUCCEED, OUR DESIRE FOR SUCCESS MUST BE GREATER THAN OUR FEAR OF FAILURE.

CHAPTER ELEVEN

Mistakes are lessons

 THE GREATEST MISTAKE YOU CAN MAKE IN LIFE IS TO BE CONTINUALLY FEARING YOU WILL MAKE ONE. - Elbert Hubbard

We live in a culture that sends mixed messages about mistakes. We're told that we learn by making them, but we still work mighty hard to avoid them. We are made to believe that it's okay not to be perfect, but on social media we are openly criticised if we do something as simple as misspell a word or have an honest opinion about something that isn't entirely politically correct.

No wonder we're all so confused!

But what if I told you that Thomas Edison failed one thousand times before he perfected the light bulb? Or that Walt Disney was fired from his job for lacking imagination and ideas?

What if I told you that, contrary to popular belief, your mistakes don't define you, but they help to shape you into the person you need to become. Everyone makes mistakes. And if you haven't already experienced a monumental one for yourself, then I'm telling you right now that you absolutely WILL! (And it's going to be OK).

We have to look at our mistakes as lessons instead of failures and know that no matter how difficult they can be to swallow at the time, they actually teach us things and give us some of our hardest and most valuable lessons in life. More than just showing us how we went wrong, mistakes teach us responsibility for our actions. They bring to light things that we may not have seen or understood before and show us how we can improve. Unfortunately, mistakes rarely feel good at the time, but they usually lead us to something better in the long run.

Without knowing the feeling of losing, winning will never feel as good. Without understanding the heartache of reaching rock bottom, being on top will never be appreciated. And without falling down, standing up again will always be taken for granted.

We need to encourage ourselves to speak honestly and try new things, even if it means possibly making mistakes otherwise how can we possibly reach our full potential in life?

One of the scariest, yet most memorable and life-changing moments of my life was the day that I woke up and decided I was going to quit my full-time job and start making Activewear for a living. Not just as a hobby, not just at nights or on weekends, but as a full-time, day in, day out actual thing!

It's easy to look back now and know that it was the right thing to do and that it was going to change my life forever. But at the time there was no guarantee of success. I didn't know where it was going to take me, how I was even going to pay my mortgage, and most people thought I was making a BIG MISTAKE!

Did I have doubts? Were people telling me not to do it? Was I scared? Yes, yes and YES! But what kept me moving forward in pursuit of my dream was that the fear of not doing it was greater than the fear of actually doing it (and possibly making a mistake.)

My advice to anyone is: be more scared of the opportunities you will miss instead of the mistakes you could make. Because if you're not pushing yourself and making mistakes along the way, then you're not actually making any decisions at all.

We grow through what we go through and I've learnt so much about myself over the years simply because I wasn't scared to make mistakes and pushed myself to try new things.

I learnt how to cut my first Activewear pieces by failing so many times and wasting metres and metres of expensive fabric. I learnt how to get the perfect fit in a pair of tights by making pair after pair for weeks at a time before I got it right. I learnt how to do media interviews by forcing myself to do them, with sweaty palms and my knees trembling. I didn't particularly enjoy pushing myself through any of these moments, but I sure did enjoy learning how to do things better and becoming more confident along the way.

Think of it like this: a child doesn't worry about falling over when they first learn to walk, they just keep trying and falling until they eventually don't fall anymore. This is how we learn! But for some reason, the older we get, the harder failure and mistakes are to accept.

Life is a zigzag – it has its ups and downs, its challenges and its triumphs. Before every win there will be numerous losses and before any breakthrough there will be so many times that we will fail. But failing at something does not make you a failure.

Remember to always seek opportunity, not security and never for one moment underestimate yourself because you're far too smart to be the only one standing in your way.

UNTOLD STORY: A VISIT FROM CUSTOMS

I can't remember exactly what year it was, but it was definitely in our first decade of business sometime in the early 2000's. It was during the government's 'Smart Country' campaign when knitting mills and factories were closing down and the government was encouraging anyone in the textile industry to retrain in another area of expertise. I was running my own factory in Brisbane, Australia at the time and I clearly remember having a constant advertisement in the paper looking for sewers with little to no applicants. The manufacturing industry in Australia was diminishing and we were forced, along with so many other brands, to move our production off-shore.

We set up a relationship with a respected manufacturer in China. We would send them design sketches and they would develop the patterns, produce samples and once they were perfected to our liking, they would produce the goods for us. Because of this process they would send us two invoices - one for development and one for the bulk production.

I can remember Bill doing his research (calling up Austrade) to get advice to confirm that we were going about things the right way. Everything was running smoothly until one day, out of the blue, Australian Customs came knocking on our door with a search warrant.

This was probably one of the scariest and most uncertain times in my life. Not just the moment Customs arrived, but the whole ordeal that ensued as a result. Basically, what happened was that Customs had opened up several of our shipping containers from China and noticed that there were two invoices - one for the development of the products and one for the product itself. We were only paying duty on the product invoice because we paid for the service separately and it was all within China so it didn't even cross our minds that it would incur any duty or taxes.

As if having Customs show up at the door wasn't distressing enough, they were also threatening a one million dollar fine and potential jail term for Bill. We thought this was the end. We thought the business was about to sink. We certainly didn't have a million dollars to bail ourselves out and the thought of jail time made us both feel sick.

At the end of the day, we held our heads high and did what we could to explain the situation and that it was an honest mistake. We ended up paying a very significant fine (which I'm not embarrassed to admit nearly crippled us) but thankfully no charges were laid.

We made a mistake and we learnt a hard (and expensive) lesson. We also learnt that in challenging times the right people are always there to support you, that you have a responsibility to make sure all of your procedures are correct and that honesty is always the best policy.

Did we think we were terrible business people because we made a pretty BIG mistake? Did we think about throwing our hands in the air and giving it all away? Did we allow this pretty major 'boo-boo' to let us feel like we had failed? No. We just picked ourselves up, brushed ourselves off, paid the fine and continued building Lorna Jane the way we knew how.

We didn't let this one mistake undo all of the other amazing things that we had accomplished. We refused to let it define who we were. We kept moving forward with our plans for Lorna Jane with even more determination and I think our success speaks for itself.

MISTAKES MAY NOT BE GREAT BUT THEY CAN BE OUR GREATEST LESSONS.

Failure is
a bruise
not a
TATTOO.

- Jon Sinclair

CHAPTER TWELVE
The importance of good habits

WE ARE WHAT WE REPEATEDLY DO. SUCCESS IS NOT AN ACTION BUT A HABIT.
- Aristotle

Everybody wants to be successful. Not everybody knows what they want to do, but everybody wants success in their life.

To be successful you need opportunity, and the one thing I know about opportunities is, they don't create themselves. But they do come into play when you combine hard work, dedication and divine timing. Or, as a result of putting yourself out there in a big way.

I could easily say that I've had a lot of opportunities in my life, but what I think is more accurate is that I have created opportunities for myself.

When I was an aerobics instructor, back in the late 1980s, I started making my own Activewear out of pure frustration that I couldn't find anything remotely fashionable to wear. I wore these cutting edge pieces to my classes, and before I knew it, everyone wanted one of my designs and out of what seemed like nowhere, an opportunity was born. After a few custom orders and discovering that my products were in high demand, I set up shop at one of the local gyms and began selling more regularly. This opportunity presented itself because I made new pieces, wore new pieces and showed up for class (wearing my new pieces), time and time again.

In hindsight, it was my commitment and consistency that created opportunities for me. I formed good habits and set myself up for success.

When it comes to success, whatever that may be for you, consistency is the key. It's just as important as passion and commitment. In fact, if you're not consistent – you're risking it all. You risk losing the promotion because you didn't show up to work. You risk coming last in the marathon because you stopped going to training. And you risk attempting another diet because you failed your last healthy eating plan.

Without consistency, you will never finish what you committed yourself to in the beginning.

The thing is, maintaining consistency isn't easy. It takes effort. It takes time. It takes patience. Effort to show up. Time working when you could be having fun. And patience to keep practising, even when you fail. Consistency is about building small, empowering habits that keep us focused on our highest priorities and goals.

It's what you do every day that impacts your life and good habits set us up for success. Our habits determine our future and if we ignore healthy habits in favour of laziness, we cannot expect to have a healthy future. The same goes for business and our dreams. If we don't keep showing up, we can't expect to achieve success.

Self-help culture claims that you can create a habit in as little as 21 days but the reality is that it's different for everyone. We have learnt most of our behaviours over a lifetime so changing or creating new habits overnight (or in 21 days) can be unrealistic. We need to be patient, take a long-term view and allow ourselves time.

Here are some of my tips to help get rid of those habits that no longer serve you and replace them with brand new ones that do.

1. Decide what you want to change...
Getting rid of bad habits is always easier when you replace them with good habits. So decide what habits you want to let go of and what new habits you'd like to replace them with.

2. Know your triggers...
Get to know what draws you back into your old behaviour and develop ways to recognise and overcome them. If you know you reach for the snack jar at 3pm every day, decide to go for a brisk walk around the block instead. If you check your emails as soon as you wake up every morning, then leave your phone in another room. And if you drink too much soft drink, then simply don't have it in the house. Know your triggers and you can change your habits.

3. Deal with the real problem...
If you are constantly over-eating or biting your finger nails because you're feeling stressed, you need to address why you are stressed and find ways to overcome or reduce it. Don't just treat the symptom, treat the problem.

4. Be patient...

It won't happen overnight, but it will happen! Remember that every habit and every person is different, so come from a place of love and be patient with yourself. Know that it will get easier over time and keep believing that it WILL be worth it in the end.

SMALL DAILY IMPROVEMENTS ARE THE KEY TO STAGGERING LONG-TERM SUCCESS.

I like to think of my good habits as rituals and my morning rituals would have to be some of the most important habits in my day. It's about setting myself up for success, and the things I do in the morning can either enhance or hinder the quality of my life.

Morning rituals should be whatever you need to do, to put yourself in the right state of mind for the rest of your day. And could be anything from pratising gratitude, to doing a little yoga or meditation, taking a sunrise walk or making a delicious smoothie.

MY MORNING RITUAL:

I wake most mornings around 5am... I try to get to bed early so that I can wake up naturally without an alarm.

I spend 10 minutes in meditation... and then write in my gratitude journal.

I pull on my Activewear... which I layout the night before to reinforce my commitment to working out and so that I have one less thing to think about in the morning.

I make a quick smoothie... I'm starving when I wake up so a smoothie is the perfect pre-workout snack.

I work out... depending on the day it can be strength training, yoga, a hike or one of my 20 minute workouts.

I take my dog for a quick walk around the block... which can also double-up as a pre-work meeting with Bill.

Have a shower, then head in to work... where I check my emails over breakfast, then start my day.

CHAPTER THIRTEEN
Goal setting

YOUR GOALS SHOULD SCARE YOU JUST
AS MUCH AS THEY THRILL YOU.

I'm not a HUGE fan of five or ten year plans but I do think if you want to achieve anything in life then you need to set specific goals along the way. Setting goals provides us with immediate incentive and long-term vision. They give us focus and help us to organise our time and resources so that we can make the most of life.

By setting a goal, you're deciding what you want to concentrate on. By setting a specific goal, you then create a greater understanding of how to achieve that goal. You need to be clear and precise with your goals, leaving no room for doubt about what you need to do. My advice is to make it something that you can easily tick off a list.

Promising that you'll 'drink less coffee' or 'sleep more' are examples of vague goals. The success of the goal isn't clearly defined, which makes it easy for us to come up with excuses when we're feeling lazy or discouraged.

A better, more specific goal would be 'I will only drink one coffee a day' or 'I will go to bed by 9.30pm during the week'. Specific goals are so much better because they give us a clear idea of what achieving our goal actually looks like. They provide us with a measurable outcome so we can clearly say that we either have or haven't achieved it.

So, how do you decide on your goals and then go about achieving them? Here are the simple steps that I take and the reasons why:

1. I decide...
I decide what it is that I want to achieve and recognise that I need to make it a priority.

2. I write it down...
For me, nothing happens unless I acknowledge it by writing it down.

3. I tell someone...
I am a strong believer in holding yourself accountable and the best way for me to do that is to tell someone. This can take some courage and vulnerability to share something that you may fail at, but it will dramatically increase your chances of success when you have the support of the people around you.

4. I breakdown my goal...
This usually involves a timeline and breaking my goal down into steps that ultimately make up the plan that will get me there.

5. I take the first step...

I don't wait for things to be perfect to make a start. Mostly because I know nothing is going to be perfect anyway. It doesn't matter how long the journey is going to be, it will only start when you take your first step.

6. I make adjustments along the way...

I try to stick to the original plan and timeline but also stay flexible if things change along the way.

7. I know that something is better than nothing...

Even when the odds are against me and it would be so easy to do nothing, I commit to doing something. If my goal is to workout every day then I do a 10 minute workout if that's all I have time for and know that any effort is better than no effort at all.

8. I celebrate...

The best part - but one that I usually forget to do because I'm quick to move on to the next goal!

While setting goals doesn't necessarily ensure that you'll reach them, it is proven that the more you think about your goals, the more momentum you create. So keep your sights on the things that you want to achieve the most, set some goals and then go out and start taking small steps to get there, one at a time.

Because a goal without a plan is simply a wish.

YOU SHOULD DO WHAT YOU SAID YOU WERE GOING TO DO BEFORE YOU GOT SUPER BUSY, THEN TOO TIRED AND PRETTY MUCH FORGOT ABOUT IT... YOU SHOULD SET SOME GOALS AND JUST GET STARTED!

– Lorna Jane Clarkson

CHAPTER FOURTEEN
The power of positivity

> *KEEP YOUR THOUGHTS POSITIVE BECAUSE YOUR THOUGHTS BECOME YOUR WORDS, YOUR WORDS BECOME YOUR BEHAVIOUR, YOUR BEHAVIOUR BECOMES YOUR HABITS, YOUR HABITS BECOME YOUR VALUES AND YOUR VALUES BECOME YOUR DESTINY.*
>
> *– Mahatma Gandhi*

I'm fortunate enough to be a naturally positive person. I innately look on the bright side of things, see the good in people and genuinely believe that anything is possible when I set my mind to it.

In fact, I think positivity is my superpower!

I believe that having a positive attitude empowers you in a way that nothing else can. And that when you choose to be positive, in the space of a single moment, your day, your week and your life can dramatically change for the better. Choose a positive attitude and suddenly you will find yourself in a different world from the one you were in before – a new world of positive possibilities.

Everything in life is energy. So we need to make sure that our energy is positive. Begin by thinking positively, which should make you feel positive, which will then make you act more positively.

One small positive thought first thing in the morning has the power to transform your entire day.

All our lives are filled with challenges that make it difficult to be positive all of the time. However, I know that choosing to be positive even when things are difficult really does make even the most challenging situations easier to bear.

So here is my go-to list for putting positivity into practise:

1. Start with yourself...

The way we think and speak to ourselves has a huge impact on how we feel about ourselves. We need to speak to ourselves in a positive way, encourage ourselves and build ourselves up so that our confidence will lift and our self-esteem with grow from strength to strength.

2. Let go of negative forces...

Spend more time with people who lift you up and less time – or no time- with the people who just bring you down by being negative and critical. This can be a little difficult, but as soon as you do it you'll find your energy shifts and everything seems more positive.

3. Take control...

I don't approach my days wondering what will happen and just letting it unfold. I take control of my life and move it in the direction I want it to go.

4. Eat good food...

I think what you feed your body directly effects how you feel so always eat nutritious food for consistent energy and positivity. Good food = good mood.

5. Share your problems...

Not that I want to burden other people, but I find if we are open and honest about our hardships with the people in our lives then it helps us to find balance, strength and perseverance.

6. Make your home (and work space) a positive place...

Yes, you guessed it – I have positive quotes and pick-me up notes all over my house and office. Try it.

7. Look to the future...

Don't spend time pining over the past, it's behind you for a reason. Keep moving forward.

8. SMILE...

Simple enough to do and proven to make you happier and more optimistic. Just try it and you will find smiling begets smiling!

9. Invest in a pet (if you can)... I know this isn't for everyone but my dog, Roger is like a positivity pill for me. He's always so happy to see me and makes me instantly forget even the most challenging of days in 5 minutes flat!

UNTOLD STORY: THAT FITTING-MODEL AD

It was the same week I started touring Australia for my fourth book 'Inspired' when suddenly, Lorna Jane was all over the press for all the wrong reasons. A new story had broken - apparently you had to be a 'perfect size 10' to work at Lorna Jane. Well, that certainly was news to me! Anyone who knows the brand knows that we have always been about empowering and inspiring ALL women to live life at 100%, so imagine my surprise.

What was happening?

I spoke to the office as soon as I could to find out that we had published an advertisement on Seek for a 'fit model' and that we had hoped to combine this role with a receptionist role so that we could offer the applicant a full-time position (we do this a lot to provide people with better jobs and more stability).

For those of you that don't know, a fit model, or fitting model is a common term in the fashion industry that describes a person who is used to check the fit, drape and appearance of a garment design. And as we make Activewear, we really need to test the movability of our products on real human bodies instead of mannequins. In general, fit model measurements need to match the brand's standard size (sample size) and at Lorna Jane (like most brands) this is a standard size small.

I remember a reporter called to ask us about the advertisement, and we explained the role and denied their accusations, but there was absolutely no mention of our comments in the story they ran!

I mean - never let the truth get in the way of a good story! Right?

It was pretty obvious what we were asking for in the ad (and there were three other ads on the website at the time, that were also asking for 'fitting models') but I was touring the country, our social engagement was at an all-time high and the media just swooped on it so that they could get in on the action!

It was crazy! I had reporters camped outside of my house and my office. Every TV channel, paper and gossip blog was talking about it and in a matter of a few days it went from an ad that combined a receptionist role with a fit model role, into a story about me and my brand discriminating against women because of their size.

I think we naturally attract girls that are fit and healthy (because we are a fitness brand) and I'd say that a lot of the girls in my stores have outgoing personalities because our brand is about positivity, but they are not all a standard size ten because as we all know – fit and healthy comes is so many different shapes and sizes.

I am sharing this story for two reasons. Firstly, because I want to set the record straight. And secondly, because I want you all to be aware of the games that the media play.

They need 'hype' so they create it themselves. And they don't care how accurate or true their claims are - or who they hurt in the process.

Although I'd spent a long time running a business, I was new to this type of exposure. My initial reaction was to ignore it because I knew it wasn't true and I figured that people would realise this for themselves and it would all go away. But I couldn't have been more wrong! The more I didn't make myself available for comment the bigger the story became. The press got the response they wanted and it remained one of the leading headlines for days.

At one stage we did send out a statement to ALL media explaining the ad and the role in detail - as I have described it to you. But not one of them printed the truth even though they knew all of the facts.

Of course the bigger it became the more devastating it was for everyone at Lorna Jane - we were being accused of something that simply wasn't true. And the thing about stories like this is that - first of all it doesn't seem to matter what the truth is - the media have an opinion and they print it. And then what is the most disappointing for people who they do this to is that these stories are 'out there' FOREVER. You just have to look up Lorna Jane and the story will appear.

We are a positive brand that exists to inspire all women around the world. Negative comments about us discriminating against women are exactly the opposite of what our brand represents. Unfortunately, I cannot help but feel that there are still some people that read this type of unfounded story and think there must be an element of truth in it for it to be publicised.

This is not the case.

Please, do not get caught up in the negativity of the press. In fact, my advice would be to limit your exposure to this type of media. My husband and I do not watch shows, read papers, magazines, or blogs that partake in this type of shameful and misleading behaviour because we think that it changes the way you think. It promotes negativity and we do not want to be fed information that is not true.

By the way, the real story about the fitting model ad is that there were over 300 applicants for the role (not one of them felt that the ad was discriminating in any way). And I'm proud to say that the successful applicant, Addie, still works for us today and is now an Assistant Designer in the creative department with me.

But that type of positive story wouldn't make the headlines, would it?

CHAPTER FIFTEEN
Decide to be happy

 HAPPINESS IS NOT ABOUT EVERYTHING BEING GOOD, IT'S ABOUT SEEING THE GOOD IN EVERYTHING.

Let me ask you a personal question - when you wake up in the morning, what's the first thing you think about? And how would your life change if your first thought every day was making a conscious effort to be happy?

I believe our happiness depends mostly on ourselves, on our decision-making and our ability to choose positive over negative. I know that sometimes it's hard to be happy. We all have bad days, weeks and even years. We go through rough patches, losses, break-ups, LIFE! But even through the most difficult of times, I believe that if we can search for the silver lining, find something to be grateful for and take a positive outlook - we will all find happiness.

The weird thing is that most of us go searching for happiness in all the wrong places. We look for it in material things, in other people and even in events or future plans. We put so much faith in 'tomorrow', hoping that it will bring something better than we have today.

Just think about all the times someone in your life has made a comment about being happy WHEN they get that new house, WHEN they lose a dress size, WHEN they get that big promotion or, god forbid, WHEN they win the lottery!

It's the idea that happiness is in the next place. A common practice that makes being happy a constantly moving target and subsequently impossible for any of us to achieve.

Happiness is not a final stop. It's the journey along the way.

The thing is happiness is not found anywhere in the external world. Happiness is something you have to nurture on the inside. It's a mixture of mindset, mindfulness and gratitude. It's about appreciating what is already wonderful in your life and being happy with the knowledge that there is always room to improve.

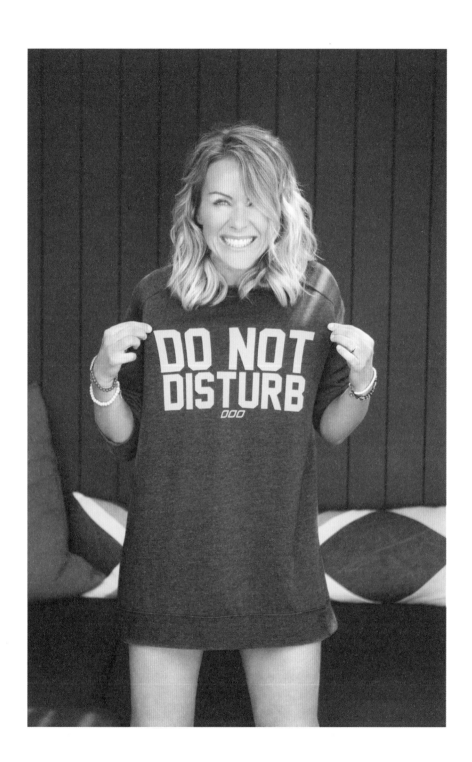

The truth is that YOU need to CHOOSE to be happy – despite the weather, despite what people think of you, despite where you are in life, despite whatever happens today, tomorrow, next week or next year. You need to try to seek out happiness every day.

So, what does it mean to be happy?

The official definition is 'feeling or showing pleasure or contentment'. But happiness is often hard to define because it means something different to everyone. What makes YOU happy can be totally different to what makes me happy which will be different again to everyone else in your life.

So let's find out what makes you happy by writing out three lists:

Things I love doing:

_____

_____

_____

_____

Things I don't love doing:

_____

_____

_____

Things I spend most of my time doing right now:

_____

_____

_____

_____

Then compare the lists – if you're spending too much time doing things that you don't love, then take this as a reality check and start spending more time doing what you love and start to be happy.

I love designing Activewear. I love working out. I love yoga. I love talking about Active Living and inspiring women to change their lives. I love long walks on the beach. I love working with my husband Bill, hiking with my dog and spending time with family and friends. I have designed a life for myself that allows me to spend more time doing the things that I love and as a result of that - I am happy.

But before you go thinking that it all sounds really easy, let me tell you that being happy takes work, and happiness is a lifelong commitment. Like everything else we want to achieve in our lives, living a happy life takes intention and practise. It also takes a bit of understanding that we won't be happy every single day, and excusing ourselves on those days.

Life can (and most definitely will) throw us some pretty big curveballs that we simply won't have the ability to catch. So it's important to remember that it's healthy to feel sad, angry, disappointed or frustrated from time to time. We're all entitled to these feelings. We're all allowed to cry, scream or do the 'couch potato' when life sucks. But, what we must remember when we face these challenging moments is that once we have our 'life sucks' reaction to them, we then have go back to choosing happiness, even if we have to chase after it a little to get our life back on track.

If life throws dirt in your face, keep it to grow some roses.

In life's most trying moments, I've learnt to seek out small servings of happiness and find simple things to lift my spirit. Things like yoga, fresh air, flowers, hot chocolate, my dog, a favourite movie, calling a friend for a chat or reading a good book. I realise that I have the power to feel any emotion that I want and know that some days will be harder than others – but when I choose to be happy the difference it can make in my life is incredible.

Here are some of my happiness tips to help you along the way:

1. Exercise...
In the immortal words of Legally Blonde's Elle Woods, 'Exercise gives you endorphins and endorphins make you happy'. Exercise is one of the most dependable mood boosters, with even just a 10-minute walk being enough to brighten your day.

2. Sleep...
At least 8 out of every 24 hours. We know that sleep helps our body recover from the day, repair itself and aid our focus. The benefits of sleep are unrivalled. But it turns out that sleep is also important for our happiness. When we don't get enough sleep, we tend to have more negative thoughts and find it hard to be happy.

3. Eat healthy food...

Your food determines your mood. So eat healthy food and both your mind and your body will thank you.

4. Spend more time with family and friends...

Research shows that spending time with the people that you love increases your feelings of happiness – and believe it or not, can make you happier than when you get a pay rise!

5. Choose happy people...

Make sure that the people you're spending time with are happy and positive because this will affect how you end up feeling too.

6. See the sun...

Spending as little as 20 minutes outside in the sunshine every day (especially in the countryside or at the beach) boosts your mood and makes you happier. There's just something about getting in touch with Mother Nature that lifts the soul.

7. Meditate...

As our world increases in speed and noise, take some time alone to meditate. This not only decreases stress but it increases longevity as well. Meditation is often credited as the single most effective way to live a happier life.

8. Count your blessings...

Happy people choose to focus on the positive aspects of their lives rather than digging up the negative. They practise gratitude and know that there is always something to be grateful for.

9. Help others...

To make yourself feel happier try helping others. Research shows that all it takes is 2 hours a week of volunteering or helping someone out to enrich our lives and spread happiness even further.

10. Plan a trip...

Simply 'planning' a holiday or break from work can improve our happiness. So even if you can't take a break right now, plan a holiday, put it on your calendar and find happiness every time you think about it.

So, what are you waiting for?

The only way to change our outer world is to change our inner world first.

And while we're talking about being happy, let me ask you, when was the last time you laughed? I mean really laughed – you know one of those whole body, cannot stop, tears-streaming-down-your-face belly laughs?

I love being around people that make me laugh. And if you rarely laugh then it's a clear sign you're taking things a little too seriously right now, and that you need to find more time for a little fun and spontaneity.

Not only does laughing make you feel good, but there are a multitude of health benefits that come with it too:

1. Your body releases endorphins... the body's feel-good hormone that can help relieve pain and promote an overall feeling of wellbeing.

2. Your body relaxes... relieving physical tension and stress for up to 45 minutes.

3. Your immune system gets a boost... by decreasing stress hormones and increasing production of infection fighting white blood cells.

So, if laughter is so good for us, how can we bring more of it into our lives?

1. Go after the funny... Watch some comedy, spend time with fun and playful friends, read funny books, watch a funny TV show.

2. Spend more time with children and animals... Kids and animals are one of the purest sources of laughter in the world. You can't help but crack up at some of the things they say and do!

3. Do silly things... I suggest doing something you loved to do as a child and haven't done in a long, long time. I'm talking cartwheels in the garden, playing Twister with some friends or spending some time in a jumping castle – laugh out loud with abandon and see how great it feels.

Life is way too short not be happy right NOW. So, make the choice to be happy and start today.

> *I THINK ONE OF MY FAVOURITE FEELINGS IS LAUGHING WITH SOMEONE AND REALISING HALF WAY THROUGH JUST HOW MUCH I LOVE THEM AND SPENDING TIME WITH THEM.*
> – Lorna Jane Clarkson

TRUE BELIEVER

Personal trainer & creator of The Fit Body Guide

Anna Victoria

WHAT IS YOUR BIGGEST ACCOMPLISHMENT?

My biggest accomplishment is being able to reach millions of women across the world and make a positive impact. It's not about the number of followers, but the number of lives I'm able to impact for the better.

NAME SOMETHING YOU ARE PROUD OF.

I'm proud of pushing myself to go after my dreams when no one else was there to push me. I was very independent from a young age, both emotionally and financially. In those cases, it's easy to become a victim of circumstance and to do the bare minimum to get by. I wanted more than that for myself; I worked as hard as necessary to make it happen and I still do.

WHAT DOES LOVING YOURSELF MEAN TO YOU?

To me, loving yourself has more than one side. It's loving yourself for who you are and where you are in the present moment. But it's also striving to be and to do better when you know you can. Just because you can be and can do better doesn't mean where you're at is any less amazing. You are amazing just as you are! Finding where those two roads cross, loving yourself in this moment while not letting the possibility of improvement inhibit you from loving yourself, is how I envision loving oneself.

WHAT DO YOU DO IN ORDER TO PRACTISE SELF-LOVE?

In order to practise self-love, I try to focus on the positive. There will always be things about ourselves we want to change or improve, but the fact that we are here, that is something to be grateful for and excited about. With that perspective, the rest of life's little problems just aren't worth disliking yourself for. Another aspect of self-love is how I treat my body, what I put into it and how I move it. The main motivation for me to continue a healthy lifestyle is because it's what I feel I deserve. I deserve to feel my absolute best and to live out this one, beautiful life I have as long as I possibly can.

WAS THERE EVER A MOMENT IN TIME WHEN YOU STOPPED BELIEVING IN YOURSELF? HOW DID YOU OVERCOME THIS?

There have been moments when I stopped believing in myself and they were always linked to when I compared myself to others. You can quickly deflate yourself by focusing on someone other than yourself so you have to be proactive about not letting those thoughts fill your head and remove yourself from whatever environment causes them.

WHAT DO YOU THINK IS YOUR BEST QUALITY AND WHY?

My ability to see the bright side. Because you can't live a positive life with a negative mind and life is too valuable and too short not to be excited to be here.

WHO IS YOUR BIGGEST ROLE MODEL & WHY?

My biggest role model isn't one person but a group of people - all the women who are mothers, businesswomen, wives, and essentially all women who are working on being their best and healthiest self while balancing so much else in their lives. Those are the people who inspire me the most.

WHAT DO YOU HOPE OTHER WOMEN WILL LEARN FROM YOUR STORY?

I hope women will learn from my story that they have everything they need within them in order to make the best life for themselves. I didn't grow up with much and I didn't have anyone encouraging me to go after my dreams. I had to encourage myself and believe in myself. If I can do it, then you can, too.

IN 25 WORDS OR LESS. WHAT IS YOUR MESSAGE TO THE WORLD?

Be your own biggest fan! You have the fire, the intelligence, and the ability to make this life more than you ever imagined.

YOUR FAVORITE INSPIRATIONAL QUOTE.

'Whether you think you can or you can't, you're right.' - Jasmine Hampton

CHAPTER SIXTEEN

Be mindful

> *THE SECRET OF HEALTH FOR BOTH MIND AND BODY IS NOT TO MOURN THE PAST, WORRY ABOUT THE FUTURE OR ANTICIPATE TROUBLES, BUT TO LIVE IN THE PRESENT MOMENT.* - Buddha

Have you ever driven somewhere and arrived wondering just how you got there? Or maybe you've turned up at work and you can't remember whether or not you brushed your teeth? These moments happen to everyone and are actually a reflection of mindlessness.

In today's culture of overwork, burnout and exhaustion we can often find ourselves going about doing what we've always done in a mindless way. And as a result, we become less conscious in our lives, sitting in cruise control and missing out on so many incredible experiences. We rush from one thing to the next always thinking about what we're about to do rather than what we are doing right NOW.

I recently read that we can spend up to 50% of our time caught up in our thoughts; effectively missing half of our lives because our minds are disconnected, thinking about the past or worrying about the future. We often fail to be present for the things that are truly important in our lives and this mindlessness has become modern day reality.

So what does it really mean to live mindfully?

Essentially, mindfulness means to be present and to live in the moment. To exist right here, right now. It's about training our attention to be where we want it to be so that we can consciously choose how to respond and react instead of existing in auto pilot mode.

The benefits of being mindful are astounding. Mindfulness is proven to lower stress, increase memory, improve sleep, make for better relationships, enhance productivity and creativity, as well as lift our overall sense of wellbeing.

Being mindful puts you back in control of your life and allows you to live with purpose. It keeps you moving forward because you are more conscious of where you are and where you want to go.

In a world that continues to get busier, it can be hard to find the time to stop and be mindful but here are my tips to getting started:

1. Only think about the present moment, the one you are currently in...
Stop dwelling on the past or worrying about the future and allow yourself to be truly present in your life right now.

2. Stop multi-tasking...
Only do one thing at a time, with purpose. When you're brushing your teeth, just brush your teeth. When you're eating, just eat. When you have a million things to do, just get through them one at a time.

3. Pay attention...
Try giving someone your undivided attention when you're with them. Listen intently when they are talking instead of thinking about the next thing you want to do or say.

4. Do less...

Look at your schedule, if you're trying to do too much then decide what's important and just do that. When you fill your day with tasks you tend to do them mindlessly – but when you decide what's important and do only those things, your sense of achievement improves because you have the time to do the important things well.

5. Find at least 5 minutes a day to do nothing...

I have to admit, for me this is quite often the Savasana in my daily yoga class - but it's really just about finding a little 'nothing time' to sit (or lie) in silence and just allow yourself time to think.

6. Slow down...

Our lives can be too much about deadlines and striving for more (I am so guilty of this!). Be aware and slow things down so that you can work on the things in your life that matter to you the most.

7. Savour your food...

Mindful people eat slowly to reclaim the pleasure of food. Interestingly, you'll find that when you eat mindfully, you eat less and digest your food better as well.

8. Improve your relationship with your phone...

Don't be a slave to technology - decide when and how often to check your phone. Put it away in meetings, when you're spending time with family and friends and especially at the dinner table every night!

9. Go for a walk...

Simply going for a walk is an excellent way to calm your mind, gain a new perspective and facilitate greater clarity and awareness. Mindful walking is about stepping away from technology, noticing and appreciating the natural beauty all around you that too often you can miss.

10. Meditate...

You can be mindful without meditation but all of the research and experts tell us that meditation is the most sure-fire way to become more mindful.

11. Do some colouring in...

This might sound a little childish but the benefits are proven! You can actually find plenty of adult colouring books specifically designed to practise mindfulness. It really forces you to slow down and focus purely on the task at hand.

Mindfulness is important because it allows us to appreciate and make the most of our lives. It's the art of being truly present, accepting the moment we're in and feeling whatever we feel without trying to resist or control it. Being mindful reminds us that our lives are good and that we should enjoy the everyday sensations of just being ALIVE.

UNTOLD STORY: BEING MINDFUL IN BUSINESS

From the very beginning, the quality of the products at Lorna Jane has been of the utmost importance to me. I wanted to design and produce the best Activewear on the planet and guarantee the workmanship, the fit and the function.

But today, it's about so much more than that.

I was in Bali last year doing a yoga course and so many people in my class were making comments about the cheap bras and tights they were wearing. They were then having totally separate conversations about animal cruelty in the food industry and making claims to being ethical when it came to what they ate, regardless of what it cost them.

I bit my tongue through quite a few of these discussions but finally had to jump in and ask them about the ethics of their cheap Activewear buys.

I mean honestly, if you can buy a pair of tights for $20 who do you think suffered? Not the company selling the tights! I can be pretty sure that it was the people working on those tights and their families. You do the maths… If you are buying them for $20, the place you are buying them from bought them for $10, which means the cost price was $5 and if 50% of the cost of the garment is fabric then it only leaves $2.50 for the freight, duties, storage, packaging, other incidentals and the person sewing them.

It has always been extremely important to me that everything about the products that we produce at Lorna Jane are both ethical and of a high standard. Would I like to give you Lorna Jane products at a cheaper price? Absolutely! But the price reflects the true cost of a quality and ethically produced product.

I am constantly approached by manufacturers who want to produce my products for me in countries where labour is cheaper and at cheaper prices but I choose to stay with the same people from a place of loyalty and because I know our people are well paid, taken care of and happy. They proudly cut, sew and manufacture your Lorna Jane Activewear pieces and are just as much a part of the Lorna Jane family as the girls in my Brisbane office and Lorna Jane stores.

I think, as consumers, we should ask more questions about the products we buy outside of the food industry. Because fashion retail prices are getting cheaper for a reason and our desire for things to be cheaper has a direct impact on the people that make these products, the environment and ultimately the world.

Today, companies need to be more mindful and take responsibility not only for the quality of the garments they produce, but for how they operate as a company. That includes the people they may not see every day.

Know that when you buy Lorna Jane you are supporting an Australian company that cares about the planet and ALL of the people on it. Our mills are ethical. Our factories are ethical. We are ethical.

And you become ethical by being mindful of the products you buy.

YOU HAVE TO BE MINDFUL BECAUSE WHAT YOU SAY AND DO HAS IMPACT LONG AFTER YOU HAVE GONE.
- Lorna Jane Clarkson

CHAPTER SEVENTEEN
Practise gratitude

 THERE ARE ONLY TWO WAYS TO LIVE YOUR LIFE. ONE IS AS THOUGH NOTHING IS A MIRACLE. THE OTHER IS AS THOUGH EVERYTHING IS A MIRACLE.

- Albert Einstein

We're all so busy, constantly chasing the extraordinary, that we sometimes forget to stop and have gratitude for the ordinary things in life that give us joy. Like the smell of coffee in the morning, clear blue skies or a soft pillow to lay your head on after a super busy day.

A grateful heart attracts miracles. And practicing gratitude regularly, gives us a more optimistic outlook and helps us to see more clearly what's positive in our lives. The more we practise gratitude, the more we realise what we actually have and learn to appreciate it.

Start your gratitude practice today by finding 3 things to show gratitude for in your life:

I am grateful for:

1. _____

2. _____

3. _____

Try writing down 3 things every morning and every night. And over a short period of time you'll begin to realise that it's the little things in life that quite often can make all the difference.

IF YOU LOOK AT WHAT YOU HAVE IN LIFE, YOU WILL ALWAYS HAVE MORE. IF YOU LOOK AT WHAT YOU DON'T HAVE IN LIFE, YOU WILL NEVER HAVE ENOUGH. - Oprah Winfrey

Gratitude can make your life better in so many ways and studies show that people who practise gratitude on a daily basis actually start to exercise more regularly, are more optimistic, feel better about their lives and are more likely to achieve their goals.

My advice would be to take it one day at a time and just start by being grateful for something as simple as your breath, the fact that you woke up this morning and that you have the opportunity to live a brand new day. Focus on what matters and choose to see the good in any situation because where your focus goes, your energy flows. And when your natural attitude is to be grateful, you automatically look at your life as a precious gift and then everything in your life becomes a blessing.

Here are some simple ways that I practise gratitude. Try them for yourself and see how different your world can become when you start each day feeling grateful:

1. Make an effort to practise gratitude... Notice your day-to-day world from a point of gratitude and be amazed at all the goodness we take for granted.

2. Keep a gratitude journal... and write down the things you are grateful for each day. Choose 3 things in the morning and then three things at night.

3. Show appreciation... Give compliments or show appreciation for someone or something at least once a day.

4. Find gratitude in your challenges... Gratitude isn't just about being grateful for the positive experiences in your life. Dig a little deeper into your past experiences to figure out what you have learned, and be grateful for how they have helped shape you into the person you are today.

5. Be thankful... Say thank you for the little things people do for you – things that you would normally take for granted.

6. Be Kind... Include random acts of kindness in your life as often as possible.

7. Avoid... negative media, negative people and movies or TV shows with destructive content.

UNTOLD STORY : I HAVEN'T ALWAYS BEEN GRATEFUL

I will admit that I had to practise gratitude in order to find it. I used to take a lot of things for granted. I used to think that because I worked hard for my success, that I was in some way entitled to it. I realise now, this is not the case. I realise that the smallest things in life can have the biggest impact and we need to count every single blessing, daily.

When I first started practicing gratitude, it felt a little unusual (writing down every little thing and being thankful.) I remember lying in bed feeling like I was going crazy in search of something new every day!

My practice was pretty basic in the beginning. I would simply write down any three things I was grateful for when I woke up in the morning and another three things when I went to sleep at night. Nothing too detailed – just simple things like my health, my family, my team at Lorna Jane and having a roof over my head. Some days it was definitely harder to think of things, but I made myself go through the process.

After about a month, I noticed that I was beginning to have a greater level of sensitivity and appreciation for the day-to-day moments in my life. Little things like my husband filling up my car with petrol for me suddenly became big things and all of my unnecessary worries felt further away.

I find that practicing gratitude is particularly beneficial in tough times. And by consciously paying more attention to the good things in my life the not so good things have become less important.

GRATITUDE TURNS WHAT WE HAVE INTO ENOUGH.
- Melody Beattie

TRUE BELIEVER

Serial entrepreneur and founder of
The Collective Hub

Lisa Messenger

WHAT IS YOUR BIGGEST ACCOMPLISHMENT?

Launching Collective Hub in March 2013. I had never worked in the media industry, let alone for a magazine. I launched a print product into a saturated market, that people said was dead or dying, with no experience, no money and no idea of what I was doing. Yet I had a big vision to empower people to be the very best version of themselves and to ignite human potential. I had no concept of just how big it would get or how far the impact would be felt. Four years in and we have become an incredible platform for our community where the magazine – which is now distributed globally – is just one small part of what we do. Every single day is new & exciting!

NAME SOMETHING YOU ARE PROUD OF.

Collective Hub and the extraordinary community we have been fortunate enough to grow. This is what keeps me going every single day. I would never have understood just how hard it would be to create something of this magnitude but even on the toughest of days, I pinch myself as to what I've been able to create.

WHAT DOES LOVING YOURSELF MEAN TO YOU?

Having an unwavering self-belief. Nurturing myself from both a physical, intellectual and spiritual perspective. Having my health as my number one non-negotiable priority.

WHAT DO YOU DO IN ORDER TO PRACTISE SELF-LOVE?

Living mindfully moment to moment. Having rituals that I practise every day from having a green smoothie, meditating (and for me this isn't sitting still for an hour at a time – it's something I practise mindfully throughout the day), journaling and writing (constantly!), doing Barre Body and / or yoga three times a week. Getting out into nature all the time. Having my home as a sanctuary. Having regular massages. Creating lots of space for me-time, alone, without social media or external distractions & noise.

WAS THERE EVER A MOMENT IN TIME WHEN YOU STOPPED BELIEVING IN YOURSELF? HOW DID YOU OVERCOME THIS?

From time to time I might get a little shaky but at no time do I ever allow myself to stop believing in myself. I have built up a tool kit of almost 15 years of spiritual practice and education. Having an unwavering self-belief is an absolute imperative. But it's been a journey; this came from not believing in myself for so many years – my entire 20s were spent living life according to other people's expectations and really having no idea of who I was.

WHAT DO YOU THINK IS YOUR BEST QUALITY AND WHY?

The ability to have fun and laugh at myself. I never take myself or anything too seriously. I have an immense ability to flip pretty much anything into a positive. The other thing is that I have a huge ability to see opportunity in pretty much anything. These two qualities keep me in flow and keep me living the very best version of me.

WHO IS YOUR BIGGEST ROLE MODEL & WHY?

I don't have one and I don't believe in having one. There are certain people who have admirable traits that I aspire to emulate: Martha Stewart, Jamie Oliver and Oprah for building extraordinary multimedia brands; Beyoncé for her tenacity; Elon Musk, Bill Gates, Richard Branson for their entrepreneurial qualities. I could go on and on and on and on. Literally I believe you can learn something from absolutely everyone on this planet and I think it's a dangerous game to pin everyone to one person. Then almost more importantly there is our community – every day their courage and tenacity just blow me away. They are what keep me going. I admire people who are relatable and attainable.

WHAT DO YOU HOPE OTHER WOMEN WILL LEARN FROM YOUR STORY?

That truly anything is possible if you have a big vision, an unwavering self belief and are prepared to back yourself.

YOUR FAVOURITE INSPIRATIONAL QUOTE:

I have so many favourite quotes…
Check out my Instagram for whatever words I am living by on that day in any moment…
@lisamessenger

CHAPTER EIGHTEEN
Surround yourself with good people

 GOOD PEOPLE BRING OUT THE GOOD IN PEOPLE.

Surrounding yourself with incredible people is a way to lift yourself up. And whether you're at work or simply enjoying life, who you choose to spend your time with has a huge impact on your energy, your emotions, your productivity and your success.

Often, this can seem like a subconscious, involuntary decision but over time (and especially as you get older) you come to realise that who you choose to have in your life is completely up to you.

My advice would be to choose carefully because these people play an important role in inspiring you, supporting you and giving you stability. I've even heard it said that over time, we actually become the average of the five people that we spend the most time with. So, who are those five people for you and are you happy with being their average?

What messages are you getting from your closest friends and family? Are they empowering and uplifting? Do they support and love you for who you are? Do they encourage you to follow your dreams and do what you love?

Or, do they fail to take you seriously when you open up about your dreams? Do they make jokes about you or try to discourage you from pursuing your passions? Do they spend a lot of time complaining? Or do they simply view the world in a negative way?

Look for people that inspire you to be a better person, that motivate you to achieve your goals, empower you to make the changes you need to succeed and cheer on your success. The people in your life also need to have their own dreams, plans and ambitions for the future so you can inspire and celebrate with each other along the way!

Remember that TIME is the most important currency in life. It cannot be bought, exchanged or refunded. It can only be spent. So make sure you spend it on those who are worthy.

Although there are no exact rules on how to attract only 'the right' people into your life here are a few tips on how to make it a little easier:

1. Be yourself...
Like attracts like, so be brave enough to be yourself and the right people will come into your life.

2. Choose carefully...
Look at your circle of friends and see whether they add value to your life or take away from it. Do they make you feel better when you're with them? If not, they should.

3. Abolish negativity...
We live in a world that surrounds us with negativity so wherever possible walk away from it - and that includes negative people. Stick with the dream-chasers, the yes-sayers and the ones who make you laugh!

4. Spend the time...
Make time to be with the people that inspire you and make you feel good. With the right people in your life there is no limit to what you can achieve.

One of the most important decisions we can make in our lives is who we choose to spend our time with so choose the people who are going to make you a better YOU.

 SHOW ME YOUR FRIENDS AND I'LL SHOW YOU WHO YOU ARE.
- Chinese Proverb

UNTOLD STORY: WORKING WITH FAMILY

People are always surprised when I tell them how many of my friends and family work with me at Lorna Jane and it puzzles me because WHY wouldn't you want to chase your dreams and build something with the people that you love.

You hear them say 'never work with family' and I will admit to hearing some family horror stories myself. But I think the reason it works for us is that our focus is not about 'money' which is what brings so many family businesses down – it is about making a difference in people lives.

So right now the official count is - one best friend, one brother-in-law, a school friend of Bill's, two sister-in-laws, one brother, one husband and one dog (head of security and happiness provider.) And over the years – my mum worked for me, my sister, my best friend's husband, my niece, Bill's sisters and so many friends.

And you don't have to be related to us to be part of the family at Lorna Jane. There are so many people at Lorna Jane that have been with us for as long as I can remember and we are proud of that. I think that the people you spend time with is important – it's nice to know that you can trust each other, that there is a genuine human connection and that we have each other's best interests at heart.

I remember quite a few years back I was out visiting one of the stores and some power lines fell on my car while I was in it! Without being too dramatic – I could have died. But I obviously didn't – and I'm telling you this because when I returned to the office everyone was so pleased to see me, that there was a line-up of people just wanting to hug me for at least an hour!

Now, that's what it feels like to work with people that you love – I'm not going to say that it works for everyone but it works for us… whether our people are 'real' family or not it just seems that over time the more you work with them the more like family they become.

CHAPTER NINETEEN

Take care of yourself

It goes without saying that you can't have an amazing life without good health. And I know from personal experience that good health starts with the simple decision to take care of yourself.

If you want to feel positive every day, if you want a body that isn't going to let you down and if you want to think clearly and have abundant energy, then you need to invest time and focus in on your health. We become the best version of ourselves by taking care of ourselves. That's what Active Living is all about.

Active Living teaches you to live at 100%. It's a shift in mindset that recognises how important being fit and healthy is to your overall success and happiness. It's about making health, your number one priority and practicing good habits on a daily basis.

Active Living makes being fit and healthy easy with the daily practice of Move, Nourish and Believe. You just have to:

1. *Move your body every day*
2. *Nourish your body with good food and doing things that you love*
3. *Believe anything is possible when you have a positive mindset and are willing to work for it.*

When you practise Move Nourish Believe every day it teaches you to make the right choices again and again until they become second nature. You get better and better and it becomes easier and easier. Before you know it you're feeling fitter and healthier, your outlook is more positive and you can't imagine living your life any other way.

When you take care of yourself you feel good about yourself and that's what Active Living is all about.

Do it over and over again until it's not just what you do, it's who you are.

I'd have to say that Active Living is my secret weapon - it keeps me fit and healthy (despite my hectic schedule) and I have no doubt that I could not have achieved all of the things in my life without it. It's effective, easy to do and most importantly it holds me accountable on a daily basis.

We instinctively know what our bodies need to be at their best – but so many of us choose to ignore it. We eat bad food, then we feel bad, we stop exercising and feel even worse. Then to top it all off we start with the negative self talk and end up blaming life and the fact that we're just way too busy to take care of ourselves!

Self-love is a key ingredient when it comes to taking care of yourself. Because when we approach Active Living from a place of love we don't feel deprived, we need less willpower and we don't jump on and off the healthy living bandwagon every few days. Instead we make choices that nurture our body and make us feel amazing. Practicing self-love means that eating whole foods is a preference not a pain, daily movement is a craving instead of a chore and taking time out to re-charge replaces pushing through and punishing our bodies.

We've already talked about loving ourselves and believing in ourselves so now I want to talk about the importance of regular exercise and the role that food plays in how we love and take care of ourselves.

Because no matter what life throws at us, or where we are on our health and fitness journey, moving our bodies, nourishing our bodies and believing in ourselves should be at the very top of our to-do list.

FALL IN LOVE WITH TAKING CARE OF YOURSELF.

MOVE. NOURISH. BELIEVE.

– Lorna Jane Clarkson

CHAPTER TWENTY
Move your body

*BECAUSE THE ONLY BAD WORKOUT IS
THE ONE YOU DIDN'T DO.*

No one can argue with the fact that our bodies were designed to move. And the more we move our bodies and take care of them, the stronger and more capable they become. Whether we choose to walk on the beach, do pilates, bounce on a trampoline or join a bootcamp – experts say that we need to move our bodies for at least 20 minutes every day.

Daily exercise is important – it reduces our risk of heart disease and type 2 diabetes. It improves mental health, relieves stress, helps with sleep, reduces our risk of osteoporosis and boosts our overall mood. So why then, is it so hard for us to continually find the discipline to workout?

We make excuses. I'm too tired. It's raining. I've had a stressful day and I just want to go home. Our brains come up with reasons not to work out all the time, but what we need to do is 'tune out' the excuses and 'tune in' to the motivation that will make us look forward to our workouts and give our bodies exactly what they need.

First things first, exercise should be enjoyable, so put in the time to find workouts that you can look forward to. Try everything! Walking, dancing, spin class, rock-climbing, barre, aerobics, swimming, cross-fit, cycling, and team sports and keep trying until you find something that you love to do.

Secondly, forget about chasing a physical outcome – do it for how it makes you FEEL. Don't do long runs, cycling classes or hot yoga if you hate them. Find activities that you're interested in, that suit your level of fitness and not because you think it's going to give you a tight butt or slimmer thighs. The more you like something, the less excuses you'll come up with and the more you will actually workout!

EAT
like you love yourself.

MOVE
like you love yourself.

SPEAK
like you love yourself.

ACT
like you love yourself.

So how do I like to move?

I definitely like to work out according to how I feel. Whether it's an energising yoga class before work, a strength session with my trainer or just a morning walk with my dog - I move my body every single day (no excuses) because I've found what works for me and what my body needs to feel capable and loved.

I strength train because it makes me feel strong, it has shaped my body in a way that cardio never could and I genuinely enjoy it. I've had the same strength coach for the last 7 years, I go with my husband and we even take Roger (our dog) along as well. We do it as a family, it works with our schedule and we get results.

On the flip side, I'm a total yogi. I love yoga because it allows me to clear my head, become lighter and let go of anything that's weighing me down physically or emotionally. Yoga also feeds my creativity and so many of my best ideas and new designs have come to me at the end of the class when I'm lying in Savasana.

There are so many types of yoga to choose from, and I like them all but my favourite is Vinyasa (or Flow yoga) because the movement has a certain magic to it that brings me into the moment and helps me forget about anything else that was on my mind.

If you're thinking of trying yoga for the first time, my advice would be to start with a beginners course which usually runs over 6-8 weeks. That way you can establish a really good understanding of the basic postures and breathing before you start to experiment with all the different types available.

The benefits of yoga are endless. And over the next few pages, you'll find some of my personal yoga practices that I do at home and when I'm traveling for energy, relaxation, to relieve stress and for jetlag. Enjoy!

SOMETIMES YOU NEED YOGA, SOMETIMES YOU NEED COFFEE AND SOMETIMES YOU NEED BOTH.

CHAPTER TWENTY-ONE

YOGA FOR ENERGY

Here are some yoga poses I do to whip up some extra energy.

3. UTTANASANA (Standing Forward Fold)

Stand with your feet hip distance apart and facing forward. Bend forwards from the hips and reach the top of your head towards the floor, knees slightly bent. Breathe deeply and feel the stretch through the back of your legs. Hold for 10 breaths. Straightening the back of your legs more with each breath.

Benefits: This pose reverses the blood flow to give you energy and releases tension from your lower back and spine.

1. TADASANA (Mountain Pose)

Stand up tall with your feet hip distance apart, shoulders down and back, and your arms by your sides. Tilt your pelvis slightly forward and extend the back of your neck straight. Close your eyes. Hold for 10 deep breaths.

Benefits: This pose improves the respiratory system, digestive system and circulation and creates an overall increase in energy.

4. UTTHITA CHATURANGA DANDASANA (High Plank Pose)

This is a type of push-up position with your arms straight and back straight. Toes are tucked and the back of the neck is straight. Hold for 5–10 breaths.

Benefits: This pose awakens your core, tones your abs and strengthens your arms.

2. UTKATASANA (Chair Pose)

Stand with your feet hip distance apart. Inhale as you raise your arms above your head and exhale as you bend at the knees into a sitting position with your knees as parallel to the ground as possible. Draw your shoulder blades into your upper back ribs as you reach you elbows back. Try to keep your weight in your heels instead of your toes. Hold for 5 breaths.

Benefits: This pose strengthens the quads, glutes and abdominals. And increases heat and energy to your body.

5. ADHO MUKHA SVANASANA (Downward Facing Dog)

Start on your hands and knees then move your hands slightly forward and spread your fingers apart. Curl your toes under and lift your knees off the ground, shooting your bottom up in to the sky to form a V-shape with your body. Your feet should be hip distance apart as you push your heels towards the ground. Hold for 5–10 breaths.

Benefits: This pose will stretch your legs, tone your arms, make you more flexible and increase energy.

6. URDHVA MUKHA SVANASANA
(Upward Facing Dog)

Start by lying face down on the ground with your legs extended out behind you. Place your hands on the ground alongside your body next to your ribs. Inhale as you press your hands firmly into the floor, pushing your upper body up and pressing your feet firmly into the ground. Hold for 5 breaths.

Benefits: This pose improves posture and strengthens and elongates your spine. It opens up your chest allowing you to feel invigorated and energised.

7. URDHVA DHANURASANA
(Wheel Pose)

Lie flat on your back with your arms by your side. Bend your knees placing your feet flat on the ground and as close to you buttocks as possible. Place your palms on the ground on either side of you head then lift your head, shoulders and hips off the ground as you straighten your arms and legs. Stay here for 5 breaths then slowly lower your body back down to the ground. Repeat twice.

Benefits: Opening your heart and taking some deep breaths will stimulate your nervous system, giving you more energy and making you more alert.

8. SALAMBA SARVANGASANA
(Supported Shoulder Stand)

Begin by lying flat on your back with your feet together and your arms by your side. Inhale and using your abdominals raise your legs and hips off the ground. Curl your torso and bring your knees towards your face then lift your hips and bring your torso perpendicular to the ground. Bend your elbow and place your hands on your lower back with your fingertips facing towards the sky. Hold for 5-10 breaths.

Benefits: If you really need some energy, get upside down! Inversions will excite your nervous system, re-awaken your mind and increase your breath and circulation.

9. BALASANA
(Childs Pose)

Sit on your heels, separate your knees to hip distance apart and then lay your arms out in front of you, resting your torso on the top of your thighs.

Benefits: This pose increases blood flow and is really good for your digestion and lower back. It's also a great to finish your practice as it's super calming for your mind and helps relieves stress and fatigue.

YOGA FOR RELAXATION

Practicing yoga is not only an effective stress reliever, but also a great way to ease the symptoms of anxiety. By transferring focus and attention to your body and the breath, yoga puts you in the present moment, calms your mind and releases any physical tension.

Just a single pose practised with awareness and slow, deep breathing can change how you feel instantly and the following yoga poses are organised in a sequence that can be practised together in this order, or individually to help alleviate stress and anxiety.

Remember to focus on your breath as you move through the poses and close your eyes if you wish to achieve a more meditative state.

1.SUKASANA
(Seated Cross-legged Pose)

Sit in a comfortable cross-legged position with your hands resting on your knees (palms down) and eyes closed. Draw the crown of your head up to the sky and your shoulder blades down your back. Focus on your breath, taking relaxed slow breaths in and out. Hold for 10 breaths.

Benefits: This pose opens your hips, lengthens your spine, amplifies the feeling of serenity and reduces tiredness.

2.ADHO MUKHA SUKHASANA
(Seated Cross-legged Forward Fold)

Start seated in a comfortable cross legged position. Then fold your hips forward and rest your palms or forearms on the ground in front of you. Try to keep your buttocks on the ground and your back straight. Hold for 5 deep breaths then swap the cross of your legs and hold for a further 5 deep breaths.

Benefits: This pose stretches your back, shoulders, hips, knees and ankles. Folding forward also reduces anxiety and fatigue and calms your mind.

3.SUPTA BADDHA KONASANA
(Reclined Bound Angle Pose)

Lie down on your back and bring the soles of your feet together and knees apart. Place your hands either alongside your waist palms up or on your belly palms down. Close your eyes. Rest here for 10 breaths.

Benefits: This pose stretches the inner thighs, groin and knees. It improves general circulation and helps relieve the symptoms of stress.

4. SUPTA MATSYENDRASANA (Supine Spinal Twist)

Lie down on your back with your legs extended straight. Open your arms out to a T-shape. Take your right knee in to your chest and gently draw it over to the left-hand side, keeping both shoulders on the ground and looking over to the left-hand side. Hold for 5 deep breaths and then repeat on the opposite side.

Benefits: This pose helps to hydrate the spinal discs, stretch your back muscles and glutes, and massage your back and hips. It also relaxes your mind and body.

5. SALABHASANA (Locust Pose)

Lie on your stomach. Keeping your back and the neck long. Inhale to extend your arms behind you lifting your legs, hands, chest and arms off the floor. Hold the height as you exhale. Inhale again, lifting and exhale as you hold this position. Repeat for 3 rounds of breath then lower and relax with your hands by your side and your head to one side.

Benefits: This pose improves your posture by strengthening the muscles of your spine, buttocks and the backs of your arms and legs and stretching your shoulders, chest, belly and thighs. It also stimulates your abdominal organs and helps relieve stress.

6. VIPARITA KARANI (Legs Up The Wall)

Lie on your back with your sit bones as close to the wall as possible and your legs running up the length of the wall. Arms relaxed by your side, palms up. Hold for 10 breaths.

Benefits: This gentle inversion is rejuvenating for the entire body as well as your mind. Allowing your body to fully relax whilst calming the nervous system and improving circulation. This pose can also help alleviate stress and headaches, boost energy and relieve lower back pain.

7. SAVASANA (Corpse Pose)

Lay down on your back with your legs and arms extended. Feet relaxed out to the side and palms facing up. Relax your whole body and close your eyes. Breathe naturally and allow your body to sink in to the ground. Stay here for at least 20 breaths or as long as you like.

Benefits: This pose relaxes your entire body, calms your mind and helps alleviate stress. It also helps to lower blood pressure and reduces headache, fatigue and insomnia.

YOGA FOR JETLAG

When you travel your energy shifts, your rhyme can become off and your body can feel fatigued. Yoga can really help with this so I thought I would share with you some of my go-to yoga poses that help ease some of the common symptoms of jetlag and that will leave you feeling fresh, healthy and ready to explore your new destination.

SURYA NAMASTAR A

(Sun Salutaion A)

A set of 12 postures that will re-vitalise you after travel. It will lengthen and strength all of your muscles and improve circulation and digestion.

*Go to movenourishbelieve.com
to watch me in action!*

1. SUKHASANA
(Seated Cross-legged Pose)

Sit with your legs crossed comfortably in front of you rooting your sit bones into the ground and draw the crown of your head up to the sky. Relax your shoulder blades down your back and gently place your hands on your thighs palms up to open and receive energy or palms down to relax.

Benefits: A gentle pose that allows you to relax and take a moment to get accustomed to your new environment. This pose helps to calm your mind, strengthen your back and gently open your hips which often feel tight after traveling.

2. SUPTA MATSYENDRASANA
(Supine Spinal Twist)

Lie down on your back with your legs extended straight. Open your arms out to a T-shape. Take your right knee in to your chest and gently draw it over to the left-hand side, keeping both shoulders on the ground and looking over to the left-hand side. Hold for 5 deep breaths and then repeat on the opposite side.

Benefits: Twists are cleansing for the body and improve digestion issues commonly caused by jetlag. They also relieve lower back pain and allow fresh oxygen and nutrients to flow to your organs.

3. SUPTA KAPOTASANA
(Supine Thread the Needle)

Lie on your back with your knees bent and both feet on the floor. Take your right knee and draw it in to your chest. Open your left knee and place your right ankle on your left knee. Interlace your fingers behind your left thigh and draw your left knee in towards your chest. Keep your head on the ground and do not strain your neck. Hold for 5 deep breaths and repeat on the other side.

Benefits: This pose helps to open up your hips and release tension that often builds up in that area after a long day of travel.

IF JETLAG IS KEEPING YOU AWAKE, TRY THESE TECHNIQUES:

THE COUNT-DOWN
Lie down in bed on your back, and close your eyes Become aware of your breathing. Slowly count the exhales backward starting with 10. Keep your focus solely on your breath. If you lose track begin again at 10.

THE SANDMAN
Lie down in bed on your back and close your eyes. Image your body filled with sand and weighted down. Observe and scan your body without moving, isolating and relaxing each body part in succession. Breathe deeply through the practice as you feel the heaviness of your body connecting with the earth.

CHAPTER TWENTY-TWO
20 minute workouts

We all get busy but let's not allow being busy to get in the way of our workouts.

When your schedule is bursting at the seams and you're tempted to skip your exercise altogether, I've found that a 20 minute workout is the perfect solution.

It could be 20 minutes of interval training on the treadmill while dinner is in the oven, it could be a quick walk around the block during your lunch break at work, or it could be some ab and butt exercises in front of the TV before you go to bed.

Every workout counts so instead of saying you're too busy, make the most of those spare moments in whatever space you have. Do your workout (no excuses) and I promise that you'll automatically become less stressed about fitting everything else you have to do into your busy day.

Here are some of my favourites that you can do almost anywhere, anytime – in a hotel room, in the corner of your office, in your lounge room or outside in the fresh air. I use them when I have a super early start, when I'm travelling or if I'm just really short on time (which seems to happen a lot!).

BOOTY WORKOUT:

30 Squats

30 Walking Lunges (or alternate standing lunges)

15 Jump Squats

30 Side Lunges

50 Bridges

 Repeat 2-3 times

AB WORKOUT:

20 crunches

Plank for 30 seconds

20 Bicycle Crunches

Plank for 30 seconds

20 Reverse Crunches

Plank for 30 seconds

Hold Boat Pose for 30 seconds

Repeat 2-3 times

CARDIO - STRENGTH WORKOUT:

30 Jumping Jacks

10 Pushups

30 High Knees

1 Minute Wall Sit

30 Mountain Climbers

20 Crunches

Repeat 2-3 times

YOGA WORKOUT:

Start standing

Forward fold

Downward dog

Plank for 20-30 seconds

Upward dog

Childs pose

Plank for 20-30 seconds

Downward dog

Low lunge

Warrior 2

Triangle

Warrior 2

Low lunge

Repeat bracket with other leg

Downward dog

Repeat 3-5 times

CHAPTER TWENTY-THREE
Get outside and walk

I love to walk. I especially love to walk first thing in the morning when it feels like the rest of the world is still asleep and it's just me, my dog and the sunrise.

Finally, a workout that has no downside! Except that it's become increasingly clear to me that so many people don't think of it as 'real' exercise.

It may not be the latest trend, it may not be flashy or cool but it's definitely a workout, and one of the things I love the most about walking is that it can be as easy or as hard as you want it to be.

If you want to really sweat try walking uphill, up some stairs or adding lunges in along the way. If you want to take it easy just slow the pace right down, take in the scenery, explore the neighbourhood and enjoy the escape from your phone and life's distractions. It's still a workout.

I walk a lot with my husband and we really enjoy the time to talk about our day, plan our weekends and just spend time together without any interruption.

UNTOLD STORY: CHANGING THE WORLD ONE WALK AT A TIME

When Bill and I go walking, we go talking. We can often talk about work and if you've spent any amount of time with us, you would know that our opinions quite often differ (dramatically). And neither of us hold back when it comes to speaking our minds or sharing our very strong opinions.

More often than not, we will be walking our dog around the neighbourhood in a heated discussion, completely oblivious to who we might pass or who can hear us. I often reflect on what the neighbours must think and have a chuckle to myself when I imagine them saying things like 'there they go again, those crazy Clarksons who can't ever seem to agree on anything!'

But I love those walks and honest, heart-felt conversations. They help us to make the right decisions and agree to move forward (maybe because we are literally moving forward together as we go.)

I also read somewhere that if you're going to argue with a man it's best to do it whilst you're walking — I don't know if it's true but it sure seems to work for us!

CHAPTER TWENTY-FOUR

Workout because you love your body

What if we all started talking about health, fitness and exercise in a more positive way? What if we could push aside the myriad of messages shouting 'change yourself' and start talking 'love yourself' instead.

I believe in such a world. I believe it should exist and I believe we all have the right to create it for ourselves.

I think it's high time that we started to workout because we LOVE our bodies, not because we are trying to change them. It's taken me a long time to get here but I feel as though I can safely say 'I LOVE MY BODY'. Sure, the little hang-ups never quite leave but they are also what make me, ME! I love what my body is capable of. I love that my body will take me where I want to go and do what I want it to do. I train hard for it and I try to do what's best for it, inside and out. And this is what I want for all women, everywhere.

I want us to stop comparing and searching and punishing ourselves. Because when we shift our focus to how our workouts make us feel instead of trying to lose weight, it changes EVERYTHING. Trust me, your body is AMAZING.

UNTOLD STORY: I USED TO CHASE
THE IMPOSSIBLE

So much of my early twenties was spent chasing the perfect physique by searching out the perfect trainer with the perfect body with the perfect formula to make me perfect.

I was looking at models and athletes and women who were taller than me, had broader shoulders than me, slimmer ankles than me and more time to dedicate to training than me. But I still thought that I would end up looking like them if I found the right workouts and put in the time. How could I possibly think for a moment that this was at all achievable?

I was chasing an idea based on what I liked about other people instead of just concentrating on my body and making it fitter and stronger and more capable. I was trying to fit a Lorna Jane sized peg into a Cindy Crawford sized hole – it was never going to fit.

What I learnt through this experience is that a) you need to always be happy with being yourself, and b) working out and eating well work best when you're doing it from a place of self-love.

Workout because you LOVE your body, not because you hate it and you're trying to look like someone else. Workout because you want to be the fittest, healthiest and happiest version of YOU.

 YOU'VE ALWAYS BEEN BEAUTIFUL, NOW YOU'RE JUST DECIDING TO BE A HEALTHIER, FITTER AND STRONGER VERSION OF YOURSELF.
- Lorna Jane Clarkson

CHAPTER TWENTY-FIVE

The Power of Activewear

> *ACTIVEWEAR WON'T CHANGE THE WORLD.*
> *BUT THE WOMEN WHO WEAR IT WILL!*
> — Lorna Jane Clarkson

Hand on heart, I truly believe that if you wear Activewear, you WILL be more active. I have been talking about this for over twenty years and from the very beginning my concept of making Activewear fashionable was so that women would wake-up in the morning, put it on and be inspired to be more active in their everyday lives.

> " I CALLED IT 'ACTIVEWEAR' BECAUSE I DIDN'T
> WANT ANYONE TO FEEL RESTRICTED TO JUST
> RUNNING OR YOGA. I WANTED YOU TO KNOW THAT
> IT IS 'TECHNICAL FASHION'. THERE ARE NO
> LIMITATIONS TO HOW YOU CAN MOVE IN IT AND
> YOU CAN WEAR IT ALL DAY, EVERY DAY AND
> BE MORE ACTIVE.
>
> *- Lorna Jane Clarkson* "

I am constantly hearing that women are challenged to find time to workout and to my way of thinking, wearing Activewear is the solution. If what you wear allows you to work more movement into your day, then it doesn't matter so much if you don't find the time to do an 'actual' scheduled work out because you have been moving your body for the entire day!

Of course the ideal is that we regularly commit to our workouts, but if this doesn't happen and you just decided to put on your Activewear, I guarantee that at the end of your day you'll have moved your body more and burned more energy than if you had opted to wear anything else.

Wearing Activewear helps us avoid the trap of feeling that it has to be all or nothing when it comes to our workouts. That we have to have the perfect space or nothing, the perfect amount of time or nothing or the perfect number of reps or nothing.

Wearing Activewear all day allows us to be more flexible and workout whenever we find the time.

Here are just a few of the things you can do when you wear your Activewear everywhere:

1. You can walk more... you can walk to work, walk to the shops or walk your kids to school.

2. You can exercise in any spare time you have... Like squatting whilst you're waiting for the kettle to boil or doing some stretches in between meetings.

3. Take the stairs instead of the escalator... Walking or running the stairs is a great leg workout so do them whenever you can. Trust me, your butt will thank you for it!

4. Get out of your inbox... I see it all the time at Lorna Jane, wearing your Activewear to work will motivate you to get up from your desk and actually talk to somebody in the office instead of sending them an email. It improves communication and boosts your metabolism and circulation.

5. Play with your kids more... wearing Activewear means you can spontaneously play with your kids and join in the fun – now that's a good idea!

For me, my Activewear is a metaphor for freedom... wearing it gives me the freedom to move and workout whenever I like. I feel relaxed, I feel comfortable, I basically just feel like I can do everything I want to do in my day without any restriction.

I JUST WANT TO WEAR ACTIVEWEAR, DRINK SMOOTHIES AND BE A LORNA JANE GIRL.

CHAPTER TWENTY-SIX

Nourishing your body

Every time you eat or drink you're deciding how you want to FEEL. If you eat junk, you're going to feel like junk. But if you eat healthy and nutritious foods you're going to feel healthy, vibrant and full of energy.

I can honestly say that the cleaner I eat, the better I feel and the better I feel, the happier I am as a person. The connection between food and mood is totally real for me and what I eat during the course of a day absolutely influences my decision-making and general attitude.

You are what you eat and eating well is about listening to your body, loving your body and giving your body what it needs. Here are some of the things I look at when deciding what to eat:

1. I know my food... I think about what I'm feeding my body and understand what each ingredient will do and how it will make my body feel. I've made it a priority to learn about the nutrients in food so that I'm empowered to make healthy decisions.

2. I eat predominantly WHOLE (aka REAL) unprocessed foods... I skip the food that comes in pretty packaging and go for real foods that are as close to their natural state as possible – freshness is key. Think fruit, vegetables, good quality meat and fish, whole grains, nuts, legumes, eggs, healthy fats and plenty of spring water. All organic and farm-friendly where possible.

3. I mix it up... To make sure I get all the nutrients my body needs, I make sure that I include a wide variety of ingredients – different food groups, different colours and different nutrients!

4. I drink plenty of water... I choose water over any other beverage and drink at least 8 glasses a day. If you find drinking water a little boring, try adding a squeeze of lemon, lime or some fresh, muddled berries for a light, fruity flavour.

When it comes to my secrets of healthy eating success, there really is nothing like:

1. Being prepared... I diligently plan and prepare. It's amazing how much easier it can be to eat nutritiously when you cook in batches and plan ahead.

2. Being well stocked... I'm often too tired to whip up an Insta-worthy meal at the end of my busy day, but I can always whip up something simple and healthy because I always keep nutritious staples on hand.

3. Having healthy snacks at the ready... both Bill and I love to snack so having healthy snack foods is essential for us. Think activated nuts, natural yoghurt, grapes, berries, homemade granola, bliss balls and homemade veggie chips.

I also try to keep it real:

1. I don't strive for perfection... I know that nothing and no one is perfect so I give myself a break whenever I go a little wayward with my food. Who doesn't crave a little (or a lot) of chocolate here and there? I know that good health is not a race to the finish-line and one bad meal or one bad day is not going to change me overnight.

2. I practise moderation... I know that healthy eating is not about dieting or deprivation so I make sure I allow myself the not-so-healthy foods I love in moderation. I eat every food group, every day but I know what to have in moderation.

There is no question that there's a powerful connection between the food we eat and how we feel. So why not move away from unhealthy food and calorie counting, and fuel your body and the life that you want to live with nutrient-dense foods that will make you feel and perform at your best?

> *THE DOCTOR OF THE FUTURE WILL NO LONGER TREAT THE HUMAN FRAME WITH DRUGS, BUT RATHER WILL CURE AND PREVENT DISEASE WITH NUTRITION.*
> – Thomas Edison

Tonics & Smoothies

Tonics and smoothies are a great way to start your day.
Whether you're in need of some energy, a little first aid or
some rejuvination, they offer the perfect solution to pack
a little more nutrition into your daily meal plan.

FIRST AID

SERVES 2
PREP TIME: 10 MINS

INGREDIENTS:
1 tablespoon ginger, grated
1 cup filtered water
Juice of 1 lemon
2 teaspoons honey

In a small saucepan, simmer ginger and water for 5 minutes. Add lemon juice and honey. Strain. To serve, dilute 50:50 with boiling water or mineral water. Enjoy warm or chilled.

Nutritional count per serving 0g total fat (0g saturated fat); 0mg cholesterol; 5g carbohydrate; 0g protein; 1g fibre; 5mg sodium; 5g sugars

ANTI-BLOATING TONIC

SERVES 2
PREP TIME: 5 MINS

INGREDIENTS:
1 cucumber
1 stalk celery
Juice of 1 lime
1 green apple
2 slices ginger
1 sprig mint
1 teaspoon chia
1 teaspoon apple cider vinegar

Add all ingredients (except apple cider vinegar and chia seeds) into your juicer. Mix juice and remaining ingredients together and serve.

Nutritional count per serving 1g total fat (0g saturated fat); 0mg cholesterol; 10g carbohydrate; 1g protein; 4g fibre; 64mg sodium; 9g sugars

LOVE POTION

SERVES 2
PREP TIME: 5 MINS

INGREDIENTS:
100g watermelon
1 cup frozen strawberries
2 slices fresh ginger
1 dragonfruit
½ cup coconut water
Juice of Lime

Add all ingredients in blender
and blend until smooth. Serve
immediately, chilled over ice.

*Nutritional count per serving 0g total fat
(0g saturated fat); 0mg cholesterol;
11.5g carbohydrate; 1.5g protein;
3.5g fibre; 15.5mg sodium; 14g sugars*

VITALITY TONIC

SERVES 2
PREP TIME: 5 MINS

INGREDIENTS:
100g mango
100g pineapple
1 cup coconut water
Juice of 1 lime
Zest of 1 lime, finely grated
1 teaspoon chia seeds

Add all ingredients in blender
and blend until smooth. Serve
immediately.

*Nutritional count per serving 1g total fat
(0g saturated fat); 0mg cholesterol;
13g carbohydrate; 2g protein;
2g fibre; 23mg sodium; 13g sugars*

PEANUT BUTTER CHOC SMOOTHIE

SERVES 1
PREP TIME: 5 MINS

INGREDIENTS:

½ banana

1 tablespoon smooth peanut butter

20g vanilla protein powder

1 medjool date

1 teaspoon cacao nibs

¼ teaspoon maca

Pinch cinnamon

Pinch nutmeg

½ cup ice

Place all ingredients in blender and process until smooth. Garnish with mixed berries and cacao nibs for a little extra indulgence!

Nutritional count per serving 14g total fat (3g saturated fat); 0mg cholesterol; 30g carbohydrate; 20.5g protein; 4g fibre; 138mg sodium; 23g sugars

REJUVINATE SMOOTHIE

SERVES 1
PREP TIME: 5 MINS

INGREDIENTS:
20g vanilla protein powder
100mL coconut milk
1 cup coconut water
½ cup frozen strawberries
1 tablespoon goji berries
Handful spinach
Pinch vanilla bean powder or paste
½ cup ice

Place all ingredients in blender and process until smooth. Top with strawberries and a sprinkle of goji berries.

Nutritional count per serving 18g total fat (14g saturated fat); 0mg cholesterol; 26g carbohydrate; 18.5g protein; 6g fibre; 110mg sodium; 25g sugars

PURIFY SMOOTHIE

MAKES 1
PREP TIME: 5 MINS

INGREDIENTS:
3 kale leaves
1 scoop collagen powder
1 pear
½ cucumber
¼ avocado
Handful mint
½ cup ice

Place all ingredients in blender and process until smooth. Enjoy chilled over ice.

ESPRESSO ENERGY SMOOTHIE

MAKES 1
PREP TIME: 5 MINS

INGREDIENTS:
¼ cup cold pressed coffee
½ frozen banana
1 cup almond milk
20g vanilla protein powder
1 medjool date
Pinch cinnamon
1 teaspoon cacao powder
½ cup ice

Place all ingredients in blender and process until smooth. Add roasted coffee beans and cacao nibs to serve.

Nutritional count per serving 10g total fat (2g saturated fat); 0mg cholesterol; 23g carbohydrate; 5g protein; 11g fibre; 33mg sodium; 23g sugars

Nutritional count per serving 8g total fat (1g saturated fat); 0mg cholesterol; 31g carbohydrate; 16.5g protein; 4g fibre; 185.5mg sodium; 26g sugars

Breakfast

Breakfast is undoubtedly the most important meal of the day. And whether it's a quick and healthy muesli bar, a delicious chia pudding or well-balanced breakfast bowl your first meal of the day should be jam-packed with healthy and nutritious ingredients.

DECADENT FRUIT-TOPPED MUESLI BARS

MAKES 10
PREP TIME: 20 MINS
COOK TIME: 25 MINS

INGREDIENTS:
1 cup oats
½ cup almonds
½ cup macadamias
½ cup pepitas
½ cup dessicated coconut
½ cup cranberries
5 dried figs, diced
⅓ cup coconut oil, melted
⅓ cup honey or rice syrup
2 eggs
2 teaspoons cinnamon
1 teaspoon ground ginger
Pinch salt
2 tablespoons honey

Preheat oven to 180°C (356°F) and line a 20 cm square cake tin with baking paper. Place all ingredients in food processor and pulse until combined. Press into lined baking tray and bake for 20-25 minutes until golden. If the top is cooking too quickly, cover with foil. Allow to cool then slice into bars. Store in refrigerator for up to one week.

We love our muesli bars for breakfast or as an afternoon snack with a dollop of coconut yoghurt, fresh figs, berries and a drizzle of honey.

Nutritional count per serving (serving size: 1 muesli bar) 26g total fat (12g saturated fat); 51mg cholesterol; 22g carbohydrate; 8g protein; 5g fibre; 35mg sodium; 16g sugars

BLUEBERRY & ORANGE CHIA DELICIOUS

SERVES 2
PREP TIME: 15

INGREDIENTS:
1 punnet blueberries
2 tablespoons chia seeds
1 large orange, peeled and cut into small segments
Juice of 1 orange
⅓ cup cashews
½ cup almond milk
1 tablespoon buckwheat
2 teaspoons maple syrup
Pinch vanilla bean paste
Pinch salt
Zest of 1 orange
Mint leaves for garnishing

Place cashews, almond milk, orange juice, orange zest, vanilla and salt in blender and process until smooth. Add in chia seeds, stirring for 30 seconds. Set them aside for 10 minutes until mixture has thickened. Layer berries, chia mixture and orange into a glass or jar, then top with buckwheat, maple, fresh berries and mint.

Nutritional count per serving 19g total fat (3g saturated fat); 0mg cholesterol; 32g carbohydrate; 10g protein; 15g fibre; 104mg sodium; 22g sugars

SWEET STRAWBERRY CHIA JAM

MAKES 2 CUPS
PREP TIME: 15 MINS

INGREDIENTS:
2 cups strawberries, stems removed and roughly chopped
¼ green apple, grated
3 tablespoons maple syrup
Juice of half a lemon
½ teaspoon vanilla powder
1 tablespoon chia seeds

In a blender, mix strawberries, apple, maple, lemon & vanilla until smooth. Simmer mixture in a saucepan for 5 minutes, until thickened. Add chia seeds and stir thoroughly. Pour into jar and allow to set for at least 1 hour. Delicious for breakfast on your favourite crusty sourdough. Keep stored in your fridge for one week.

Nutritional count per serving (serving size: 1 tablespoon)
0g total fat (0g saturated fat); 0mg cholesterol;
4g carbohydrate; 0g protein; 1g fibre; 1mg sodium;
4g sugars

SWEET & SAVOURY SUNDAY MORNING SPELT CREPES

MAKES 6 CREPES
PREP TIME: 40 MINS
COOKING TIME: 5 MINS

CREPE INGREDIENTS:
1 cup white spelt flour
2 eggs
350mL almond milk
20g rapadura sugar
(sweet crepes, omit for savory)
30g coconut oil, melted
Pinch salt
Extra coconut oil for frying

Place all ingredients in blender and mix until combined. Stand batter for 30 minutes or make ahead to time and chill overnight. To cook, heat coconut oil in a pan on high heat and add ¼ cup of batter at a time, evenly coating the pan in batter. Cook for 1-2 minutes each side or until golden. Repeat with remaining mixture.

SWEET FILLING:
Strawberries & vanilla labne

Nutritional count per serving 1g total fat (1g saturated fat); 4mg cholesterol; 6g carbohydrate; 2g protein; 1g fibre; 17mg sodium; 6g sugars

INGREDIENTS:
2 cups strawberries, quartered
½ cup vanilla bean labne or natural greek yoghurt
1 tablespoon honey
Pistachios, crushed

Stack crepes with labne and top with fresh strawberries, blueberries and crushed pistachios.

SAVOURY FILLING:
wood smoked salmon, asparagus & goats cheese

INGREDIENTS:
150g wood smoked salmon
50g soft goats cheese
2 teaspoons olive oil
1 bunch asparagus, quartered
1 sprig dill
Himalayan salt and black pepper
1 wedge lemon

Panfry asparagus in olive oil for 3 minutes. Add in smoked salmon to warm through. Fill crepe with salmon, goats cheese, asparagus, dill and season well with salt and pepper. Serve with a lemon wedge for extra zing.

Nutritional count per serving
6g total fat (2g saturated fat);
20mg cholesterol;
0g carbohydrate; 8g protein;
1g fibre; 367mg sodium;
0g sugars

THE BALANCE
BREAKFAST BOWL

SERVES 2
PREP TIME: 10 MINS
COOKING TIME: 25 MINS

INGREDIENTS:
1 sweet potato, thinly sliced into rounds
1 bunch brocollini, halved and blanched
2 eggs, soft boiled
4 leaves tuscan kale, finely chopped
1 avocado, sliced
1 mild chilli, finely diced
Juice and zest of a lemon
1 tablespoon olive oil
2 tablespoons honey

Preheat oven to 180°C (356°F) and line an oven tray with baking paper. Brush sweet potato with coconut oil, paprika and salt, place on tray. Bake for 20-25 minutes until golden. In the meantime, in a frypan heat remaining coconut oil and sauté kale with chilli for 3 minutes. Season kale well with salt.

Make dressing by mixing together the lemon juice, lemon zest, honey and olive oil. In serving bowls, arrange sautéed kale, baked sweet potato, sliced avocado, broccolini, sauerkraut with one boiled egg on top per serve. Pour over dressing and serve with a wedge of lemon for an extra boost of citrus.

Nutritional count per serving 53g total fat (24g saturated fat); 255mg cholesterol; 32g carbohydrate; 17g protein; 13g fibre; 239mg sodium; 14g sugars

VERY VEGGIE
MINI FRITTATAS

SERVES 2
PREP TIME: 30 MINS
COOK TIME: 20-25 MINS

INGREDIENTS:
2 cups sweet potato, grated
6 eggs, lightly beaten
1 red capsicum
1 cup baby spinach
1 sprig basil, finely chopped
1 tablespoon pine nuts
1 tablespoon olive oil
Pinch Himalayan salt and black pepper

Preheat oven to 180°C (356°F). Line a muffin tray with baking paper in 6 muffin holes. On a seperate tray, place capsicum in oven and roast for 15-20 minutes until soft. In the meantime, in a medium frypan, heat olive oil and sauté sweet potato until softened, then press into the base of the lined muffin tin. Once capsicum is cooked and slightly cooled, peel skin, remove seeds and slice capsicum into small strips. In a medium sized bowl, whisk eggs. Add pine nuts, basil and seasoning. Pour egg mixture over the sweet potato in the muffin tray. Add a few leaves of baby spinach and some capsicum to the each portion of egg mixture. Bake for 20-25 minutes until frittatas are golden. Serve with a simple side salad of greens and cherry tomatoes.

Nutritional count per serving (serving size: 1 frittata)
19g total fat (4g saturated fat); 509mg cholesterol;
13g carbohydrate; 16g protein; 4g fibre; 166mg sodium;
7g sugars

Soul Bowls

Soul bowls are like smoothies - packed with nutrition and easy to digest. From the simplicity of a cleansing green soup to my deliciously spicy coconut and ginger poached chicken broth, these are some of my all-time favourites and can be served in small portions at the beginning of a meal or in larger portions as a main.

COCONUT & GINGER POACHED CHICKEN BROTH

SERVES 2
PREP TIME: 15 MINS
COOKING TIME: 15 MINS +
10 MINS REST

INGREDIENTS:
400g chicken breast
400mL coconut milk
2 thumbs ginger, finely chopped
2 shallots, finely chopped
3 stems coriander, leaves removed and finely chopped
Juice of a lime
¼ teaspoon Himalayan salt

BROTH
400mL chicken broth
1 zucchini, sliced thinly into noodles
¼ butternut pumpkin, slice thinly into noodles
1 red capsicum, finely sliced
10 snow peas, finely sliced
Splash of tamari

In a non stick frypan heat coconut oil and sauté ginger, shallots and coriander for 3 minutes. Add coconut milk, lime and salt and bring to a simmer. Add chicken breast and simmer covered for 15-20 minutes until chicken is cooked through; turning over half way through cooking to cook evenly. Rest for 10 minutes. Allow to cool slightly and shred with a fork or thinly slice.

In a saucepan simmer broth with vegetables for 4 minutes. Add in chicken and poaching liquid. Simmer 3 minutes to heat through. Add tamari and coriander leaves.

Nutritional count per serving 41g total fat (34g saturated fat); 118mg cholesterol; 24g carbohydrate; 55g protein; 8g fibre; 926mg sodium; 19g sugars

CLEANSING GREEN SOUP

SERVES 4
PREP TIME: 15 MINS
COOKING TIME: 15 MINS

INGREDIENTS:

2 stalks celery, finely chopped

1 head broccoli, cut into florets

1 zucchini, roughly chopped

1 cup peas (fresh or frozen)

1 leek, finely chopped

2 garlic, finely chopped

1 bunch parsley, roughly chopped

400g tin cannellini beans, rinsed and drained

½ teaspoon cumin

500mL chicken or vegetable stock

1 tablespoon olive oil

Lemon zest and finely chopped parsley to garnish

Heat olive oil in saucepan and saute leek, garlic and celery for 4 minutes. Add in all remaining ingredients and simmer 15 minutes. Allow to cool slightly and then puree in food processor until smooth. Season well with salt and pepper. Garnish with lemon zest and parsley.

Nutritional count per serving 7g total fat (1g saturated fat); 0mg cholesterol; 20g carbohydrate; 15g protein; 16g fibre; 691mg sodium; 8g sugars

INGREDIENTS:

400g chicken thigh or firm tofu, diced

2 cups diced butternut pumpkin

1 red onion, finely chopped

1 clove garlic, crushed

1 thumb ginger, grated

2 coriander stalks, finely chopped

1 red capsicum, diced

1 300mL tin coconut milk

1 cup chicken broth or stock

1 tablespoon shiro (white) miso paste dissolved in 1 tablespoon boiling water

2 tablespoons red curry paste

2 tablespoon coconut oil

Salt and pepper to taste

2 tablespoons sunflower or mung

In a medium frypan, heat half the coconut oil and fry chicken thigh in batches until golden. Set aside. Heat remaining coconut oil and saute red onion garlic, ginger, coriander stalks for 4 minutes. Add red curry paste and fry for 1 minute or until aromatic. Add chicken, pumpkin and remaining ingredients and stir to combine.

Cover and simmer, stirring occasionally for 20 minutes or until chicken and pumpkin are cooked. Garnish with coriander leaves and sprouts. Delicious served with brown or wild rice for a heartier meal.

NOURISH TIP: *Use firm tofu in place of chicken and vegetable stock as a vegetarian option*

WARMING PUMPKIN MISO CHICKEN CURRY

Nutritional count per serving 58g total fat (37g saturated fat); 200mg cholesterol; 25g carbohydrate; 54g protein; 9g fibre; 1930mg sodium; 19g sugars

SERVES 2
PREP TIME: 15 MINS
COOKING TIME: 20 MINS

CARROT & GINGER WINTER WARMER
WITH CORIANDER CASHEW CREAM

SERVES 2
PREP TIME: 25 MINS
COOKING TIME: 30 MINS

INGREDIENTS:
4 carrots, peeled and roughly chopped
1 sweet potato, peeled and roughly chopped
1 brown onion, diced
2 garlic cloves, crushed
2 thumb ginger, finely grated
1 teaspoon fresh turmeric or ¼ teaspoon dried
½ teaspoon cumin
1 teaspoon ground coriander
500mL vegetable or chicken stock
1 tablespoon tamari
Salt and pepper to taste
2 tablespoon coconut oil
¼ cup roasted cashews to garnish

CASHEW CORIANDER CREAM
INGREDIENTS:
½ cup cashews
½ cup water
1 bunch coriander leaves
2 spring onions, roughly chopped
1 green chilli, seeds removed (optional)
Juice of a lime
¼ teaspoon Himalayan Salt
¼ teaspoon black pepper

TO MAKE SOUP: Preheat oven to 180°C (356°F) and line an oven tray. Place sweet potato and carrot on tray and coat in half the coconut oil and ground coriander and cumin. Roast for 25 minutes.

Meanwhile In a medium saucepan heat remaining coconut oil and saute onion, garlic, ginger and fresh turmeric for 3 minutes. Once cooked, add roasted vegetables to saucepan and all remaining ingredients and simmer 15 minutes. Once cooked, and all to blender and blend until smooth. To serve, drizzle with cashew coriander cream and garnish with roasted cashews and microherbs.

TO MAKE CREAM: Place all ingredients in blender and process until smooth and creamy. Add more water if too thick.

Nutritional count per serving 39g total fat (13g saturated fat); 0mg cholesterol; 60g carbohydrate; 19g protein; 23g fibre; 1564mg sodium; 31g sugars

Salads

One of my favourite things to eat is salad. And I'm not talking about a few leafy greens on a plate but a delicious satisfying meal filled with amazing textures, colours and flavours. I just know I'm doing my body a favour by eating them and what better way to get all of your vitamins and nutrition for the day without compromising on taste?

CRISPY PEAR & GOJI KALE SALAD

SERVES 4
PREP TIME: 10 MINS

INGREDIENTS:
1 bunch kale, shredded
1 crispy pear, finely sliced
2 tablespoons goji berries
2 tablespoons goats cheese, crumbled
2 tablespoons almonds, lightly crushed in mortar & pestle
1 tablespoon olive oil
2 teaspoons Apple Cider Vinegar
2 teaspoons maple syrup
Himalayan salt

Place kale into a large bowl. Pour over olive oil and massage thoroughly into kale leaves. Add crispy pear, goji berries and almonds, mix through. In a small ramekin, mix together apple cider vinegar and maple syrup. Top salad with crumbled goats cheese and drizzle with the maple vinegar dressing. Add a pinch of salt to taste.

Nutritional count per serving 10g total fat (2g saturated fat); 7mg cholesterol; 11g carbohydrate; 4g protein; 4g fibre; 101mg sodium; 11g sugars

RAINBOW SUPERFOOD SALAD

SERVES 4
PREP TIME: 10 MINS
COOKING TIME: 5 MINS

INGREDIENTS:
1 zucchini, noodle sliced
¼ butternut pumpkin, noodle sliced
2 teaspoons macadamia oil or olive oil
Pinch Himalayan Salt and black pepper
1 cos lettuce, shredded
½ red capsicum, sliced
½ yellow capsicum, sliced
½ avocado, diced
2 spring onions, finely sliced
1 handful mint, finely chopped
1 handful coriander, finely chopped
2 tablespoons macadamias, chopped

DRESSING

INGREDIENTS:
Juice and zest of a lime
1 thumb grated Ginger
1 teaspoon honey
¼ cup coconut milk
¼ teaspoon salt

Blanch zucchini noodles and
pumpkin noodles in boiling water
for 1 minute. Toss noodles in 2
teaspoons macadamia oil, salt
and pepper. Add all remaining
ingredients to bowl. Whisk dressing
ingredients together in a small bowl
and pour over salad.

*Nutritional count per serving 30g total fat
(8g saturated fat); 0mg cholesterol;
26g carbohydrate; 12g protein; 13g fibre;
172mg sodium; 22g sugars*

BAKED PUMPKIN & POMEGRANATE SIDE SALAD

SERVES 4
COOK TIME: 25 MINS

INGREDIENTS:
½ small pumpkin
½ pomegranate
¼ cup natural yoghurt
Handful fresh coriander
Handful crushed cashews

Cut pumpkin into 1cm thick crescent shaped pieces. Place in baking tray with a drizzle of olive oil and a sprinkling of Himalayan rock salt. Bake on 200°C (400°F) for 25 minutes, or until pumpkin is lightly golden. Place baked pumpkin on a serving dish.

Dollop with natural yoghurt and sprinkle with pomegranate, coriander and crushed cashews. Delicious hot or cold as a main or the perfect side dish.

Nutritional count per serving 18g total fat (3g saturated fat); 3mg cholesterol; 20g carbohydrate; 8g protein; 6g fibre; 302mg sodium; 15g sugars

NOT SO POTATO SALAD

SERVES 4-6
PREP TIME: 30 MINS

INGREDIENTS:
1 medium size sweet potato
2 eggs
Handful fresh green beans
Half a floret of cauliflower
1 cup lightly roasted cashews
2 teaspoons Dijon mustard
Juice of 1 small lemon
1 spring onion
Parsley for garnishing

Boil eggs until yolk is hard. Boil sweet potato until soft and skin starts to peel away. Boil cauliflower for 10-15 minutes until soft but still firm. Blanch green beans. Set aside and allow to cool.

For the cashew cream 'mayo': In a food processor, blend cashews, Dijon mustard and lemon juice and a pinch of salt until mixture is smooth.

Once all vegetables have cooled, mix through cashew cream 'mayo' and garnish with finely chopped spring onion and a light garnish of parsley.

The perfect side dish for any occasion!

Nutritional count per serving 21g total fat (4g saturated fat); 127mg cholesterol; 25g carbohydrate; 15g protein; 9g fibre; 126mg sodium; 10g sugars

Mains

At the end of a busy day, it's important that your meals are quick and easy to make but also delicious and packed full of nutrients. And the recipes in this chapter are some of my go-to favourites, which I hope you will enjoy enough to make your favourites too.

LENTIL, SWEET POTATO & PINE NUT 'SAUSAGE' ROLLS

MAKES 8
PREP TIME: 25 MINS
COOKING TIME: 35 MINS

INGREDIENTS:
1 sweet potato, diced 1 cm
1 small red onion, finely diced
1 clove garlic, crushed
¼ cup sundried tomatoes, chopped
3 stalks parsley, stems removed and leaves chopped finely
1 egg
½ teaspoon ground cumin
1 teaspoon ground coriander
¼ teaspoon chilli flakes
1 tablespoon black sesame seeds
¼ cup pine nuts
2 x 400g tin of brown lentils
1 packet of mountain bread wraps (or similar square wraps)
¼ teaspoon Himalayan salt
¼ teaspoon pepper
2 tablespoon coconut oil
Coconut oil spray

Preheat oven to 180°C (356°F) and line a baking tray. Bake diced sweet potato in half the coconut oil for 20 minutes. Meanwhile, heat remaining coconut oil in frypan and saute onion and garlic until cooked. Add in pine nuts and cook for another minute. Add to food processor with drained lentils, sundried tomatoes, parsley, cumin, coriander, chilli, egg, salt, pepper and roast sweet potato and pulse 2-3 times, or until the mixture resembles and 'mince' consistency.

Place mountain bread on board and place 1 cup of mixture evenly across the end of the mountain bread in a 'sausage' shape. Roll to enclose filling and place onto a lined baking tray. Once all mixture has been rolled, spray rolls with coconut oil and sprinkle on sesame. Bake for 20-25 minutes until golden. Let cool slightly and cut into 5cm lengths. Serve immediately.

Eat with your favourite sauces or side salad.

Nutritional count per serving (serving size: 1 sausage roll) 10g total fat (3g saturated fat); 32mg cholesterol; 35g carbohydrate; 12g protein; 10g fibre; 585mg sodium; 9g sugars

CHICKEN SHITAKE
SAN CHOY BOW BOATS

SERVES 2
PREP TIME: 10 MINS
COOKING TIME: 15 MINS

INGREDIENTS:
400g organic chicken mince

40g shitake mushroom,
soaked and chopped

2 garlic, crushed

1 thumb ginger, grated

4 shallots, finely sliced

1 carrot, diced

4 stems coriander, finely chopped and
leaves set aside

1 teaspoon dried coriander

½ teaspoon cumin

2 teaspoons white sesame seeds

1 teaspoon black sesame seeds

2 tablespoons tamari

1 tablespoon maple syrup

2 tablespoon coconut oil

Coriander leaves to garnish

Sliced spring onions to garnish

Sliced red chilli to garnish

Cos lettuce cups to serve

In a fry pan, heat half the coconut oil over medium heat and saute shallots, garlic, ginger, carrot, coriander stems and shitake mushrooms and cook for 2-3 minutes. Remove from pan. Add remaining coconut oil and fry chicken mince in batches for 5-7 minutes until golden. Add garlic mixture back into pan with chicken and all remaining ingredients and stir fry for 4 minutes. Serve mixture in firm lettuce cups.

Nutritional count per serving 25g total fat (12g saturated fat); 158mg cholesterol; 16g carbohydrate; 44g protein; 7g fibre; 1484mg sodium; 13g sugars

ROSEMARY & LENTIL
NOT SO 'MEATBALLS'
IN HEIRLOOM TOMATO SAUCE

SERVES 2-3
PREP TIME: 15 MINS
COOKING TIME 20 MINS

INGREDIENTS:
1½ cups cooked brown lentils
(use tinned if in a hurry)
1 tablespoon olive oil
2 cloves garlic, crushed
1 leek, finely sliced
2 sprigs rosemary, stem removed and
finely chopped
1 egg
½ teaspoon dried oregano
½ teaspoon dried basil
½ teaspoon paprika
⅓ cup rolled oats, ground
1 tablespoon pine nuts
1 tablespoon tamari
Salt and pepper to taste

Preheat oven to 180°C (356°F) and line
a baking tray. In medium sized frypan
heat olive oil over medium heat and
sauté leek and garlic for 3-5 minutes.
Place garlic mixture and all remaining
ingredients in a food processor and
pulse until combined. Mixture should
resemble a mince consistency and
stick together when squeezed in the
palm of your hand. Spoon ¼ cup of
mixture in the palm of your hand and
roll together to make a ball. Repeat
this with all of your mixture. Heat
olive oil in a pan and place balls in
frypan and cook 3 minutes each side.
Transfer to oven tray and bake for
15 minutes until firm to touch.

*Nutritional count per serving 30g total fat
(4g saturated fat); 127mg cholesterol;
47g carbohydrate; 23g protein; 23g fibre;
1625mg sodium; 20g sugars*

HEIRLOOM TOMATO SAUCE

INGREDIENTS:
1 tin crushed cherry tomatoes
1 punnet heirloom cherry tomatoes
2 cloves garlic, crushed
4 shallots, finely chopped
½ cup chicken stock
¼ teaspoon Himalayan Salt
¼ teaspoon black pepper

In a medium frypan heat olive oil and
sauté shallots for 4 minutes. Add
garlic and cook for another minute.
Add all remaining ingredients and
simmer 15 minutes.

ZUCCHINI PASTA
2 zucchinis, sliced with julienne
peeler or mandolin

To assemble, place zucchini pasta
in bowl and top with lentil balls and
tomato sauce.

NOURISH TIPS: *If gluten free
use gluten free oats or gluten free
breadcrumbs.*

*If you want a meat version swap
lentil for turkey or beef mince.*

*If you want to make these
vegan, replace egg with
1 tablespoon flaxseed
meal.*

SEEDED CRUMBED CHICKEN SCHNITZEL

SERVES 2
PREP TIME: 10 MINS
COOK TIME: 10 MINS

INGREDIENTS:

2 chicken breasts,
sliced horizontally in half

2 tablespoon sesame seeds

2 tablespoons pepitas

2 tablespoons sunflower seeds

2 tablespoons pine nuts

¼ teaspoon Himalayan salt

¼ teaspoon black pepper

1 tablespoon coconut oil

Grind seeds and seasoning in spice grinder and sprinkle onto plate. Dip chicken breast into seed mixture to coat well. Heat coconut oil in non-stick pan over medium heat and pan fry 4-5 minutes each side until golden and cooked through. Serve with thinly sliced green apple, mint and lemon or your favourite side salad.

Eat with your favourite sauces or side salad. We love this with our not-so potato salad or a serving of thinly sliced green apple and mint.

Nutritional count per serving 43g total fat (13g saturated fat); 118mg cholesterol; 2g carbohydrate; 57g protein; 4g fibre; 205mg sodium; 1g sugars

ROASTED NORI & SESAMI SALMON

WITH AVOCADO CORIANDER PESTO

SERVES 2
PREP TIME: 10 MINS
COOK TIME: 12 MINS

INGREDIENTS:

2 skin off salmon fillets

1 tablespoon sesame seeds

1 sheet nori

Pinch Himalayan sea salt

2 teaspoons coconut oil

Pinch black pepper

AVOCADO CORIANDER PESTO

1 avocado

1 handful fresh coriander, chopped

2 spring onions, roughly chopped

Juice of a lime

¼ teaspoon Himalayan salt

¼ teaspoon pepper

Preheat oven to 180°C (356°F) and line a baking tray. Place sesame seeds and nori in spice grinder or blender (with grinder blade) with salt and pepper and blend. Coat salmon in sesame and nori mixture and panfry in coconut oil over medium high heat for 4 minutes each side. Finish off in oven until cooked to your liking.

To make pesto: Place all ingredients in blender and process until smooth.

We love this with a simple side salad of mixed greens or the crispy pear and kale salad on p.154.

Nutritional count per serving 49g total fat (13g saturated fat); 99mg cholesterol; 2g carbohydrate; 36g protein; 5g fibre; 192mg sodium; 1g sugars

Desserts

One of the most challenging parts of eating healthily is finding desserts that are good for you. And in this chapter I have chosen recipes that are mostly based on fruits and nuts and taste so good that you'll find it hard to believe they are actually good for you.

CHOC HAZELNUT SPREAD

MAKES 1 ½ CUPS
PREP TIME: 15 MINS
COO TIME: 10 MINS

INGREDIENTS:
1 cup hazelnuts
3 tablespoons cacao
3 tablespoons coconut syrup or maple syrup
3 tablespoons coconut oil
½ cup water
¼ teaspoon Himalayan salt

Preheat oven 180°C (356°F) and line a baking tray. Place hazelnuts on tray and roast for 8 minutes. Place in the centre of a clean tea towel and make a bundle around nuts, then rub on a benchtop to remove hazelnut skins. Place skinned hazelnuts into food processor and blend for 3 minutes or until a paste has formed. Add in cacao, coconut syrup, coconut oil and blend to combine. Add in water and salt and blend to for a smooth paste. Refrigerate until required. Remove from refrigerator 10 minutes before required to allow paste to soften. Store this in your refrigerator for 1 week.

Nutritional count per serving (serving size: 1 tablespoon) 8g total fat (3g saturated fat); 0mg cholesterol; 3g carbohydrate; 1g protein; 1g fibre; 17mg sodium; 2g sugars

HAZELNUT CRUNCH FUDGE

MAKES 12 PIECES
PREP TIME: 3 MINS
CHILL TIME: 1HR

INGREDIENTS:
1 cup choc hazelnut spread (recipe p.168)
1 cup shredded coconut
½ cup chopped hazelnut

Place hazelnut spread and coconut in food processor and blend until smooth. Line a 20cm x 15 cm plastic container with baking paper. Pour in fudge, and spread out evenly. Pour over extra hazelnuts and press into mixture. Place in freezer to chill. Once chilled, remove from tray and cut into 12 pieces. Keep these in the fridge until you are ready to eat. Store in your refrigerator for 1 week.

Nutritional count per serving (serving size: 1 piece) 12g total fat (7g saturated fat); 0mg cholesterol; 4g carbohydrate; 2g protein; 2g fibre; 18mg sodium; 3g sugars

INDULGENT CACAO CHIP (N)ICECREAM

SERVES 2
PREP TIME: 10 MINS

INGREDIENTS:
2 frozen bananas, chopped
3 tablespoons cacao powder
1 tablespoon cacao nibs
½ cup coconut milk
2 tablespoons maple syrup
1 teaspoon vanilla
Pinch Himalayan salt

Place all ingredients in blender and process until smooth. Top with cacao nibs and serve immediately.

Nutritional count per serving
11g total fat (8g saturated fat);
0mg cholesterol; 43g carbohydrate;
5g protein; 7g fibre; 102mg sodium;
30g sugars

BLISSFUL BERRY (N)ICECREAM

SERVES 2
PREP TIME: 10 MINS

INGREDIENTS:
2 frozen bananas (peeled)
1 cup frozen berries
½ cup coconut water
1 teaspoon vanilla paste

Place all ingredients in blender and process until smooth. Top with fresh berries and serve immediately.

Nutritional count per serving 1g total fat (0g saturated fat); 0mg cholesterol; 31g carbohydrate; 3g protein; 5g fibre; 9mg sodium; 22g sugars

SWEET & SPICY PEANUT BUTTER (N)ICECREAM

SERVES 2
PREP TIME: 10 MINS

INGREDIENTS:
2 frozen bananas, peeled and chopped
¼ cup peanut butter
½ cup coconut water
1 teaspoon maple syrup
⅛ teaspoon cayenne pepper
Pinch salt

Place all ingredients in blender and process until smooth. Top with your favourite chopped nuts and an extra sprinkle of cayenne pepper. Serve immediately.

Nutritional count per serving
35g total fat (6g saturated fat);
0mg cholesterol; 37g carbohydrate;
18g protein; 7g fibre; 337mg sodium;
26g sugars

BLISS BALLS

MAKES 12
PREP TIME 10 MINS + CHILL TIME

RICH MOCHA TRUFFLE BALLS

INGREDIENTS:
½ cup almonds
½ cup macadamias
½ cup raisins or medjool dates
¼ cup cacao powder
¼ cup almond nut butter
1 tablespoon cold pressed coffee
Pinch Himalayan salt
Pinch cinnamon

Place almond and macadamias in food processor and pulse until roughly chopped. Add in all remaining ingredients and process until combined. Roll 2 tablespoons of mixture into balls. Chill in refrigerator for 1 hour. Dust with cacao before serving (optional).

COCONUT BERRY BLISS BALLS

INGREDIENTS:
1 cup cashews
½ cup freeze dried raspberries or frozen raspberries
2 tablespoons goji berries
1 cup dessicated coconut
3 tablespoons cashew butter
1 teaspoon lemon zest
Pinch Himalayan salt

Place all ingredients in blender and pulse until well combined. Roll 2 tablespoons of mixture into balls, then roll in desiccated coconut. Chill in refrigerator 1 hour.

NOURISH TIP: if you are pack these in lunch boxes use freeze dried raspberries.

Nutritional count per serving (serving size: 1 ball) 16g total fat (2g saturated fat); 0mg cholesterol; 7g carbohydrate; 5g protein; 3g fibre; 22mg sodium; 6g sugars

Nutritional count per serving (serving size: 1 ball) 15g total fat (6.5g saturated fat); 0mg cholesterol; 7g carbohydrate; 4g protein; 3g fibre; 34.5mg sodium; 3g sugars

GREEN GODDESS ENERGY BITES

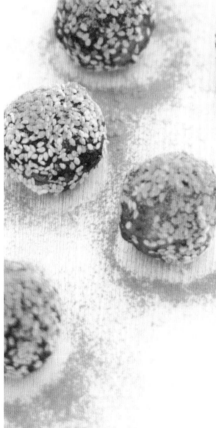

INGREDIENTS:

½ cup almonds

½ cup cashews

½ cup dessicated coconut

½ cup raisins

1 tablespoon rice syrup

1 tablespoon coconut oil

2 tablespoons sesame seeds

2 teaspoons orange zest

2 tablespoons orange juice

1-2 teaspoons spirulina or green powder (depending on taste)

Pinch Himalayan salt

Place nuts in blender and pulse to breadcrumb consistency. Add all remaining ingredients except sesame seeds and blend well to combine. Roll 2 tablespoon sized balls in sesame seeds and refrigerate 1 hour. Dust with green powder before serving.

Nutritional count per serving (serving size: 1 ball) 14g total fat (5g saturated fat); 0mg cholesterol; 10g carbohydrate; 4g protein; 2g fibre; 18mg sodium; 7g sugars

CHAPTER TWENTY-SEVEN
Find balance

Like most of you, my days (and weeks) are literally jam-packed and getting busier. From the time I open my eyes in the morning until the time I fall asleep at night, I feel like I'm balancing competing priorities and constantly weighing everything I do against everything else I should be doing.

You know what it's like - should I sleep in or exercise? Should I check my emails over breakfast or have a conversation instead? Should I pack my lunch or grab something from the shop? Should I have another coffee or try some green tea? Should I do a late yoga class or stay home with my family? Should I cook dinner or grab takeout? Should I catch up on my emails or go to sleep instead?

Our lives are a constant series of choices, weighing up the pros and cons of every decision, as we try to fit everything that we want to do into the hours that we have available. It's a balancing act and it's constant.

We often talk about finding work-life balance but does that concept even exist? Or should we be talking about finding work-life harmony in our lives instead.

It's my opinion that over the past decade the term 'work-life balance' has been used (and over-used) to imply that there is a perfect balance between career and lifestyle - which I think is impossible to achieve. And, as a result, so many people are chasing a false reality.

There is a reason there are so many 'get rich quick schemes' out there tempting people with the ideology of less work and more money – only to leave people disappointed (or broke) when the reality of what it takes to have success in anything in life clicks in!

We have to forget about trying to balance work and life and think about it as balancing all of our decisions, every day against a whole list of competing priorities. We need to aim to integrate all elements of our lives (work and play) the best that we can.

Sometimes that might mean that work takes priority for a duration of time (like right now as I try to finish writing this book) and other times it may be our family. Whatever it is be OK with that and ensure that YOU give whatever priority you have decided to focus on, 100% for that period of time.

For some of us that might mean working long and hard for big bursts of time and then taking regular short breaks where we can carve out special time for ourselves and our family. For others it might mean taking a break from your emails each afternoon until the kids are in bed so you can spend quality time with them every day. It will be different for everyone and ever-changing as our lives evolve.

UNTOLD STORY: WHEN PEOPLE TELL ME THEY
WANT WORK-LIFE BALANCE

I cannot tell you the amount of times I have asked someone in an interview 'why do you want to work for Lorna Jane?' And they say, 'I'm looking for work-life balance', and then go on to tell me that they want to work less to have more time for other things in life.

It never ceases to amaze me that people think working at Lorna Jane is more about finding a good work-life balance than it is about actually working. Yes, we make time for yoga, green smoothies and all the rest but at the end of the day, we work our butts off in all the hours in-between. We do what it takes to make things happen. We work here because we believe wholeheartedly in what we are trying to achieve - to inspire women. And sometimes that means long days, overtime and the odd Saturday here and there.

What I DO hope people gain from working for us is a job that satisfies their dreams and desires more than any other job. I hope people find a place where they can grow, learn and constantly find inspiration. The real answer I'm looking for is that they love what Lorna Jane stands for and they want to be a part of it.

Working at Lorna Jane gives you opportunities like no other working environment. We are successful because we have a vision and we work extremely hard to make it a reality. We consistently go the extra mile to chase down our dreams and constantly challenge ourselves to achieve more.

I don't believe that having a job where you can leave the office on time every day equates to 'work-life balance'. It's about finding a job that you are so passionate about that you let a little of it in to your personal life because it's part of you. I don't completely believe in 'leaving work at work' and I think the sooner we find what we truly love to do every day, the sooner we will find balance and the better our work-life relationship will become.

There is no secret formula, self-help book or perfect company to work for, that will give you a balanced life. It takes work, and a lot of it is simply analysing your needs and the needs of the people that you love in your life in order to achieve a balance that works for you.

In reality your idea of balance can be whatever you want it to be. But if you need a little help getting started, here are some of the things that I do to create balance in my life on a regular basis:

1. Take care of yourself... You cannot accomplish anything if you're unhealthy. Get plenty of rest, exercise and eat properly. You may think that you can burn the candle at both ends, eat junk food, do very little exercise and still function adequately. But the reality is that you will burnout eventually.

2. Have priorities... Balance does not mean cramming in every activity possible. Look at your values and decide what is important to you. You may be in the process of building a career, starting a family or going to school. Depending on what stage you're at in life will determine where you put your energy and focus. Avoid becoming overwhelmed by juggling too many priorities at once.

3. Be efficient... Create an efficient mindset, be organised and plan ahead. Take time at the beginning of the week to look at what needs to be done and put everything into a schedule – including things that are likely to be put to the side such as your workouts and time with family and friends.

4. Embrace the unexpected... Rather than getting stressed and upset if things don't go to plan, learn to roll with the punches and readjust your plan. There may be times when a career or family crisis needs your immediate and undivided attention. When that happens do whatever it takes, and take time to rest and rejuvenate when things get back to normal.

5. Always be positive... Begin each day with the intention of making the most of it. When you're juggling so much, things don't always go to plan. But an important part of living a well-balanced life is learning how to deal with unforeseen events and uncertainty. When you practise not letting things get to you (especially in the morning when you look at your day and say WOW!) You will not only learn to live a well-balanced life but one with less stress as well.

> *THERE IS NO SUCH THING AS WORK-LIFE BALANCE. EVERYTIIING WORTH FIGHTING FOR UNBALANCES YOUR LIFE.*
>
> *- Alain De Botton*

CHAPTER TWENTY-EIGHT
Dealing with stress

Stress is a modern day reality and when you give 100% to your life you can almost guarantee there'll be days when things get a little overwhelming, you forget to slow down and before you know it you're exhausted - and you start to feel stressed.

Stress can come into our lives in many forms - things like work, deadlines, financial trouble, arguments, and even congested traffic. At first, we may seem irritable, snappy, unable to think clearly and possibly make a few silly mistakes. However, if the pressure continues and we fail to do anything about it our performance can drop, we can develop symptoms of anxiety and eventually depression.

So what can we do?

Stress is the natural reaction our bodies creates to deal with negative pressures, and to manage it we need to find the balance between too little and too much of this pressure in our lives. Too little pressure leaves us without motivation to do anything, and too much pressure can be counterproductive, because we get stressed and can't see a way to get everything done!

The reality is that no one can avoid stress completely so we need to recognise when the pressures are accumulating in our lives and take action to deal with them – we need to take charge and start to do things differently.

We need to listen to our bodies and take control of our stress by:

1. Getting some fresh air... The vitamin D from sunlight boosts our serotonin levels and getting outside to take in the sights, sounds and fresh air helps to re-direct our focus away from our problems.

2. Finding refuge in your rituals... Whether it's taking a bath before bed, walking the dog or listening to your favourite playlist whilst you're driving home from work – our bodies crave routine, and focusing on our rituals increase our body's ability to deal with stress.

3. Getting out of your head... Do something that needs your undivided attention like team sport, rock climbing or dance class. By forcing yourself to concentrate and be in the moment you can actually put all of your worries aside for a while.

4. Look at what you're eating... Focus on eating real foods instead of running to the vending machine and eating junk. Sugar and processed foods will only mess with your blood sugar levels and leave you feeling even more stressed!

5. Exercising (walking, yoga or stretching)... While it is easy to let your workout schedule slide when you're feeling a little overwhelmed, keep in mind that exercise is quite possibly the best stress buster ever! Exercise increases your serotonin levels, regulates sleep, boosts your energy and lowers the symptoms of mild depression – making you calmer and more focused.

6. Taking a bath... Water has an innate calming effect on your mind and your body. So take a good, long soak in the tub and try adding a few drops of lavender oil for its stress-reducing properties.

7. Getting more sleep... Aim for seven to nine hours per night and even consider taking a couple of short naps on the weekend when you are going through more stress than is usual for you. Avoid caffeine and excess alcohol and make your bedroom a tranquil oasis with no reminders of the things that can cause you stress.

8. Breathing deeply and slowly... Sending a message to your brain to calm down and relax.

9. Sharing the problem with someone that is a good listener... Just talking to someone about how you feel can be helpful. Talking things through can help you find solutions to stress and put your problems in perspective.

10. Learning to say 'no'... A common cause of stress is having too much to do and too little time to do it in. Learning to say 'no' to additional or unimportant requests will help reduce your stress and help you develop more self-confidence.

11. And finally, know that sometimes the most productive thing you can do is absolutely nothing.

THE GREATEST WEAPON AGAINST
STRESS IS OUR ABILITY TO CHOOSE
ONE THOUGHT OVER ANOTHER.

– William James

CHAPTER TWENTY-NINE
Meditation

When it comes to meditation, I get the feeling that most people think it's difficult and that it's something only a gifted few can do. When in fact, meditation is simply an approach to training your mind, similar to the way that fitness is an approach to training your body.

Buddha was once asked what he gained from meditation and his answer was this:

> *NOTHING! HOWEVER, LET ME TELL YOU WHAT I HAVE LOST: ANGER, ANXIETY, DEPRESSION, INSECURITY, FEAR OF OLD AGE AND DEATH.*

All you really have to do is find out the basics, commit to the practice and do it day after day until it starts to feel natural. Just think of it like any other discipline and remember that it takes practise to consistently score goals in netball, it takes practise to balance in shoulder stand and it will take practise (and a little time) to get into the zone and achieve the benefits of meditation.

There are so many different meditation techniques to explore, but if you're just getting started here are a few tips (and things that I do) when I meditate on a daily basis:

My guide to meditation:

1. Select a suitable space...
Choose somewhere you can sit easily with little to no disturbance. Maybe a corner of your bedroom or a quiet spot somewhere in your home. Make it a sacred space by keeping a chair or meditation cushion there as a reminder that it's your meditation space.

2. Select a regular time...

Choose a time that fits in with your schedule. If you're a morning person, experiment with sitting down to meditate before breakfast. If the evening suits you best, then maybe after work or before going to bed. Begin with just 10 or 20 minutes at a time.

3. Find a posture...

Sit comfortably on your chair or cushion without being too rigid. Let your body be firmly planted on the earth (or seat) with your hands resting easily, your chest relaxed and your eyes gently closed. Consciously feel your body and soften any obvious tension. Let go of any habitual thoughts or plans and bring your attention to the sensation of your breath.

4. Breathe...

Probably the most important element of a good meditation is getting your breath in check. Take a few deep breaths to settle your mind and then let your breath become natural. Feel the sensations of your breath carefully, make no effort to control your breath and just relax. Inhale the calm, exhale the madness. Slowly, slowly.

5. Focus...

After a few breaths your mind will probably begin to wander. When you notice this, mindfully acknowledge the thought with a word like 'thinking', 'wandering' or 'hearing' and simply bring your attention back to your breathing.

6. Time...

Maintain this meditation practice for ten minutes to start, and only begin to lengthen the time if you feel you need more. Don't force yourself to extend your meditation if you're not ready. In time you might feel that you can extend it up to 25 minutes. Everybody is different so it's important that you do what feels right for you.

I meditate every day, usually in bed before I go to sleep or as soon as I wake up in the morning. Sometimes I prop myself up on some pillows and other times (especially at night) I simply lie in Savasana. I can't say anyone has noticed but I sometimes take a sneaky meditation break during the day in my office and I've also been known to sit cross-legged on an aeroplane seat if I feel the need for a little zen!

For one minute
just walk
OUTSIDE
Look up at the sky.
Stand there in
SILENCE
& contemplate
how WONDERFUL
life is.

CHAPTER THIRTY

Celebrate how far you've come

 THE MORE YOU CELEBRATE YOUR LIFE, THE MORE THERE IS IN LIFE TO CELEBRATE.
– Oprah Winfrey

Recognise how far you've come and thank yourself for all of the amazing things you have managed to achieve along the way by developing a practice of writing love letters - to yourself.

I know this may sound a little strange to some of you, but writing a love letter to yourself is a really great exercise in self-love that allows you to reflect on all of your challenges, hard work and accomplishments and celebrate just how far you've come.

It's a moment to sit back and marvel at your life. The sadness that has softened you, the lessons that have pushed you to grow and the fun moments that have made it all worthwhile.

I usually write a letter to myself once a year around the New Year and start the process by finding a quiet space where I can sit and escape the day with a little meditation. This clears my mind and creates an open-hearted space of love and self-discovery.

I've included my most recent love letter to give you some inspiration for your own...

Letter to
Me.

Dear Lorna,

Wow, what a journey. And what a wild rollercoaster ride it's been. I can't believe you've just finished another book!

It's been a dream come true but A LOT of hard work. I'm glad you always kept going even though I realise so many things could have held you back. I'm glad that you learnt to block out the naysayers along the way. People think what you do is easy for you, but I know that nothing worthwhile is easy, although sometimes we wish it was. I know your confidence has grown immensely but I also know how much you have to push yourself sometimes to get there. You weren't born with it, you worked for it and that's what I'm most proud of.

What I really want to say is thank you. Thank you for committing to your dreams and showing up with consistency. Thank you for sticking to your guns and fuelling yourself with unwavering self-belief. Thank you for taking responsibility and accountability for your actions and always speaking up. Thank you for learning from your mistakes and growing through your greatest challenges. It certainly doesn't get easier but you do get better at it.

I don't believe you'll ever feel a full sense of achievement because you're always so quick to move on to the next adventure. I think we've done so many great things together but I know your dreams are limitless. I want you to stop for a moment and listen to your own advice – be mindful, be grateful, learn to relax every so often and always dream BIG. You have a big responsibility, so use it wisely. And remember –we never, never, never give up! Because who knows where we could end up together…

Love, LJC X

Define SUCCESS on your own terms. Achieve it by your own rules

and build a
life that you're
PROUD
to live.

— Anne Sweeney

Sincere gratitude and a super big thank you to all the people that helped make this book possible. Thanks for your support, love, encouragement, advice and general greatness.

SPECIAL THANKS TO:

My husband Bill for his endless love and unwavering belief in me... having you by my side every day is a gift like no other.

To my family and friends for surrounding me with endless love and support, even (and especially) when I work too much.

To Layne, Lisa and Anna - thank you for sharing your wisdom and showing all the women in the world what it means to be a trail-blazer in your chosen field and a True Believer in yourself and what you do.

Big thanks to my amazing team at Lorna Jane – to those that worked tirelessly with me on this book, but also the ones that picked up the slack for me when I had to write instead of designing, planning or marketing with you.

Hugs, kisses and oodles of thanks to Kelly - it would have been impossible without you. You have been my partner in crime from start to finish and I thank you from the bottom of my heart for your confidence in my message and your determination to make it heard.

Thanks also to Lorae, for perfecting every page with me – and accepting all of my last minute changes with a smile.

And last but not least, a big heart-felt thank you to all of the women that love and support Lorna Jane - you are the reason we exist and my daily inspiration to not only design great Activewear, but to promote Active Living and encourage you to live at 100%.

About the author

In 1985, a young girl in Brisbane, Australia initiated the thinking of gym wear being worn as a fashion lifestyle garment. Could women actually put on their workout clothes and want to go to the gym, exercise more and feel empowered? Let's face it, Wonder Woman wore Lycra, why not everyone else? It is this innovation and creative thinking that has seen Lorna Jane Clarkson not only coin the phrase 'Activewear' but also become creator of the Activewear category.

Lorna's unique way of life has transformed not only what women wear all over the world but also how her followers think about health and wellness. Her very own philosophy of Active Living and the daily practice of Move Nourish Believe are the foundations of her life and her brand. It is her undying passion, determination and drive that continues to inspire women across the globe to constantly strive for more.

This book summarises her life in a practical sense, delving into her real-life experiences, her inspiration and her unwavering self-belief. Without the combination of these characteristics, there would be no 'Lorna Jane', no 'Activewear' and no philosophy of 'Active Living'. Lorna is a true testament to the fact that hard work, commitment and a 'never give up' attitude are key ingredients to success.

Index

Conversion chart

MEASURES

One Australian metric measuring cup holds approximately 250ml; one Australian metric tablespoon holds 20ml; one Australian metric teaspoon holds 5ml.

The difference between one country's measuring cups and another's is within a two- or three-teaspoon variance, and will not affect your cooking results. North America, New Zealand and the United Kingdom use a 15ml tablespoon.

All cup and spoon measurements are level. The most accurate way of measuring dry ingredients is to weigh them. When measuring liquids, use a clear glass or plastic jug with the metric markings.

The imperial measurements used in these recipes are approximate only. Measurements for cake pans are approximate only. Using same-shaped cake pans of a similar size should not affect the outcome of your baking. We measure the inside top of the cake pan to determine sizes.

We used large eggs with an average weight of 60g.

OVEN TEMPERATURES

The oven temperatures in this book are for conventional ovens; if you have a fan-forced oven, decrease the temperature by 10-20 degrees.

	°C (CELSIUS)	°F (FAHRENHEIT)
Very slow	120	250
Slow	150	300
Moderately slow	160	325
Moderate	180	350
Moderately hot	200	400
Hot	220	425
Very hot	240	475

LIQUID MEASURES

METRIC	IMPERIAL
30ml	1 fluid oz
60ml	2 fluid oz
100ml	3 fluid oz
125ml	4 fluid oz
150ml	5 fluid oz
190ml	6 fluid oz
250ml	8 fluid oz
300ml	10 fluid oz
500ml	16 fluid oz
600ml	20 fluid oz
1000ml (1 litre)	1¾ pints

LENGTH MEASURES

METRIC	IMPERIAL
3mm	⅛in
6mm	¼in
1cm	½in
2cm	¾in
2.5cm	1in
5cm	2in
6cm	2½in
8cm	3in
10cm	4in
13cm	5in
15cm	6in
18cm	7in
20cm	8in
22cm	9in
25cm	10in
28cm	11in
30cm	12in (1ft)

DRY MEASURES

METRIC	IMPERIAL
15g	½oz
30g	1oz
60g	2oz
90g	3oz
125g	4oz (¼lb)
155g	5oz
185g	6oz
220g	7oz
250g	8oz (½lb)
280g	9oz
315g	10oz
345g	11oz
375g	12oz (¾lb)
410g	13oz
440g	14oz
470g	15oz
500g	16oz (1lb)
750g	24oz (1½lb)
1kg	32oz (2lb)

First published 2017.
Published by Lorna Jane.
Printed by Bauer Media Books.

Author: Lorna Jane Clarkson
Creative Director: Lorna Jane Clarkson
Senior Creative: Kelly Bastaja
Senior Designer: Lorae Misipeka
Food Editor: Jasmine Norton
Food Photographer: Kelly Bastaja
Food Stylist: Sheldon Hikaiti
Lifestyle pPhotographers: Jason Zambelli, Louise Smit, Tyra Gunnis
Printed in China.

National Library of Australia Cataloguing-in-Publication entry:
Author: Clarkson, Lorna Jane
Title: Love You
ISBN: 9780648093107